INDIANS

BLACK HAWK, *C...*
OSCEOLA, *Clark*
POCAHONTAS, *Se...*
PONTIAC, *Peckh...*
SACAGAWEA, *Sey...*
SEQUOYAH, *Snot...*
SITTING BULL, *S...*
SQUANTO, *Stevenson*
TECUMSEH, *Stevenson*

NAVAL HEROES

DAVID FARRAGUT, *Long*
GEORGE DEWEY, *Long*
JOHN PAUL JONES, *Snow*
MATTHEW CALBRAITH PERRY, *Scharbach*
OLIVER HAZARD PERRY, *Long*
RAPHAEL SEMMES, *Snow*
STEPHEN DECATUR, *Smith*

NOTED WIVES and MOTHERS

ABIGAIL ADAMS, *Wagoner*
DOLLY MADISON, *Monsell*
ELEANOR ROOSEVELT, *Weil*
JESSIE FREMONT, *Wagoner*
MARTHA WASHINGTON, *Wagoner*
MARY TODD LINCOLN, *Wilkie*
NANCY HANKS, *Stevenson*
RACHEL JACKSON, *Govan*

SCIENTISTS and INVENTORS

ABNER DOUBLEDAY, *Dunham*
ALBERT EINSTEIN, *Hammontree*
ALECK BELL, *Widdemer*
CYRUS MCCORMICK, *Dobler*
ELI WHITNEY, *Snow*
ELIAS HOWE, *Corcoran*
ELIZABETH BLACKWELL, *Henry*
GAIL BORDEN, *Paradis*
GEORGE CARVER, *Stevenson*
GEORGE EASTMAN, *Henry*
GEORGE PULLMAN, *Myers*
GEORGE WESTINGHOUSE, *Dunham*
HENRY FORD, *Aird and Ruddiman*
JOHN AUDUBON, *Mason*
JOHN BURROUGHS, *Frisbee*
JOHN DEERE, *Bare*
JOHN FITCH, *Stevenson*
LEE DEFOREST, *Dobler*
LUTHER BURBANK, *Burt*
MARIA MITCHELL, *Melin*
ROBERT FULTON, *Henry*
ROBERT GODDARD, *Moore*

...l. MORSE, *Snow*
..., Guthridge
..., *Higgins*
..., ORVILLE WRIGHT,
...CHARLIE MAYO,
...ree

... and ...LEADERS

BETSY ROSS, *Weil*
BOOKER T. W............on
...., *Mason*
J. STERLING MORTON, *Moore*
JANE ADDAMS, *Wagoner*
JOHN PETER ZENGER, *Long*
JULIA WARD HOWE, *Wagoner*
JULIETTE LOW, *Higgins*
LILIUOKALANI, *Newman*
LUCRETIA MOTT, *Burnett*
MOLLY PITCHER, *Stevenson*
OLIVER WENDELL HOLMES, JR., *Dunham*
SUSAN ANTHONY, *Monsell*

SOLDIERS

ANTHONY WAYNE, *Stevenson*
BEDFORD FORREST, *Parks*
DAN MORGAN, *Bryant*
DOUGLAS MACARTHUR, *Long*
ETHAN ALLEN, *Winders*
FRANCIS MARION, *Steele*
GEORGE CUSTER, *Stevenson*
ISRAEL PUTNAM, *Stevenson*
JEB STUART, *Winders*
NATHANAEL GREENE, *Peckham*
ROBERT E. LEE, *Monsell*
SAM HOUSTON, *Stevenson*
TOM JACKSON, *Monsell*
U. S. GRANT, *Stevenson*
WILLIAM HENRY HARRISON, *Peckham*
ZACK TAYLOR, *Wilkie*

STATESMEN

ABE LINCOLN, *Stevenson*
ANDY JACKSON, *Stevenson*
DAN WEBSTER, *Smith*
FRANKLIN ROOSEVELT, *Weil*
HENRY CLAY, *Monsell*
HERBERT HOOVER, *Comfort*
JAMES MONROE, *Widdemer*
JEFF DAVIS, *de Grummond and Delaune*
JOHN F. KENNEDY, *Frisbee*
JOHN MARSHALL, *Monsell*
TEDDY ROOSEVELT, *Parks*
WOODROW WILSON, *Monsell*

James J. Hill

Young Empire Builder

Illustrated by William K. Plummer

James J. Hill

Young Empire Builder

By Mildred Comfort

 THE **BOBBS-MERRILL** COMPANY, INC.
A SUBSIDIARY OF HOWARD W. SAMS & CO., INC.
Publishers • INDIANAPOLIS • NEW YORK

LIBRARY OF CONGRESS CATALOG CARD NUMBER: 68-55147

PRINTED IN THE UNITED STATES OF AMERICA

To Elizabeth Wedel
Granddaughter of Dorothy Braucht

1473738

Illustrations

Numerous smaller illustrations

Contents

★   ★

Books by Mildred Comfort

HERBERT HOOVER: BOY ENGINEER
JAMES J. HILL: YOUNG EMPIRE BUILDER

James J. Hill

Young Empire Builder

A Log House
with a Bookshelf

ONE LATE SPRING NIGHT in 1843 five-year-old
James Hill went to sleep, lulled by rain on the
cabin roof. The rain would be good for his father's newly planted corn.

Yesterday James had walked along rows, drop-
ping three seeds into each hole. His father, following with a hoe, had heaped up the earth over
them and tapped each mound down.

The Hill farm covered fifty acres of land two
miles from Rockwood, Ontario, Canada. Next
fall James and his sister Mary-Eliza would walk
to the Rockwood School. His brother Alex
would be too young for school.

The Hill farm was not very good. There were many rocks in the soil, some of which Mr. Hill had used to build fences. Mrs. Hill always took time from her very busy life to grow lilacs around the log cabin.

A crash awakened James out of a sound sleep. He rushed to a window to look out as lightning flashed in the sky. Outside he could see what had happened. The lightning had struck and toppled a tree near the cabin.

At daylight James heard his mother's voice, calm as always. She had said so often, "It will be the happiest day of my life when the last tree that could reach the cabin has been cut down. Only then will I feel safe."

Alex, on the bunk beside James in the lean-to, stirred. Mary-Eliza, on a cot near the big bed with the patchwork quilt, roused. Father was already busy, making a fire in the cookstove, and Mother was preparing the cornmeal mush.

"Is it my tree, Father?" James called out. He pointed out the great oak where a woodpecker had once lived. "I'll bet it's a hundred years old. Look at that big gnarled trunk."

"Yes, son, it's your tree," his father called back. "The storm saved me the hard work of cutting it down. We'll get right to work on it. You children can carry off the branches. I'll cut up the trunk with my crosscut saw."

"I'll help you," said James.

He struggled into his clothes, his rough shirt, work pants, and moccasins. Some day he would get shoes. Father had promised him leather shoes with brass toes to take scuffing.

The family enjoyed the breakfast of cornmeal mush with maple syrup and tea. There was good cream, too. It had been skimmed off the crock in which the milk had stood overnight.

After the dishes were cleared, Mr. Hill got down the plush-covered Bible from the bookcase and brought it over to the table. The others listened closely while he read a psalm. Then he thanked God for his mercy in saving the cabin from the falling tree. Mr. Hill was not a big man, but he had a deep voice.

Often he recited poems from Robert Burns, and he played the flute. He showed the children words from *Walker's Dictionary*, when there was time. Today he let the Bible open itself to the family record page, saying the usual blessing on all that was written there.

James became restless, seated beside his brother Alex on a bench. Quietly he got up and looked over his father's shoulder. He never tired of looking at the records written in ink in Anne Dunbar Hill's careful script.

The page in the Bible was beautiful. It was decorated with fine, golden scrolls. Trumpeting angels proclaimed great tidings of joy.

The firstborn in the Hill family had been a

14

son, who was no longer living. The oldest son, in the old family tradition, had been named after his father. The Hills had decided to live up to this custom.

James could read the familiar names. Mary-Eliza, named for her two grandmothers, had been born on Christmas day, 1835. He saw his own name next, James, born September 16, 1838. The record of his own birth had been written in an especially firm hand, as though Anne Dunbar Hill rejoiced that she now had a second son, one she could name James.

Then came his little brother, Alexander Samuel Dunbar, who was born September 6, 1839. Affectionately he would be called Alex, but when he grew up he would become A.S.D. Hill. While James and Mary-Eliza gazed at the sacred page, Alex played with the carpet rags in his mother's work basket. How cheerful the room looked with the spatter of bright, braided rugs!

Father soon became restless and brisk. He set the Bible back and went into the clearing to study the tree. He milked the cow and fed her in the roughly built barn. He spread some grain for the chickens in a little log enclosure, and he poured some fresh milk into a small trough for a grunting pig.

James went outdoors and paused swiftly to enjoy the faint fragrance of wild plum blossoms coming from the woods. He gathered eggs from nests in the barn and carried loads of cordwood to the woodbox. Then he added several rolls of birchbark that he and Alex had peeled off an old fallen tree in the woods. His mother liked the birchbark for building a quick fire in the kitchen stove.

Already Mr. Hill had done much work on the fallen tree. He had brought out his big crosscut saw to cut through the stubborn bark and the heavy timber of the trunk. James soon tired of hacking away at some of the branches with his little axe. "Please, Father, let me help you saw the wood," he begged.

"No, your mother will help," said his father. Already Mrs. Hill had made the beds, washed the dishes, and swept the house. Too, she had started a kettle of soup.

Like a man, she took hold of the great cross-cut saw. Together, she and Mr. Hill, like a magnificent team, began the arduous task of cutting through the trunk of the tree. The saw moved back and forth, back and forth, with the rhythm of a poem or song.

The hours flew. Mary-Eliza was sent into the house to tend the soup, to put more wood in the stove, and to set the table for the noon meal. Alex picked up sticks and made a neat pile to dry in the sun.

Later Mrs. Hill quit sawing and went to the house. James jumped for the handle to take

her place. "Whee!" he cried gleefully, as he grabbed it tightly with his hands.

His father moved the saw through the wood and lifted James off his feet. James swung up into the air, lost his footing, and fell. "Are you hurt?" asked his father.

"Only my feelings," James admitted as he got up and dusted himself off.

"Sometimes you bite off more than you can chew," said his father.

"It won't always be like that," said James. "Soon I can do all kinds of work."

The big oak which had fallen proved to be a good solid tree. At dinner Mr. Hill explained that it contained very fine hardwood. "Possibly we can sell some of our other oaks for making furniture. Then we won't be quite so poor."

"We're not poor," Mary-Eliza said with pride. She tossed her curls. "We're the only people in the settlement who have a bookshelf."

"And a flute," Alex added, laughing.

"I like the books and the flute," James put in, "but I wish that we had a horse and wagon. Then, Father, you would not have to carry the grist to the mill on your back."

"What we need," the father said, "we shall have. The Lord will provide."

The parents looked at each other in quiet understanding. "Tell them," the mother said.

"I have made plans," Mr. Hill said, "to buy a horse and wagon. The corn crop will pay for it—at least I hope it will."

James hoped that his father could pay for the horse and wagon when he brought them home. He hoped that the corn crop would be good. He would help take care of the corn.

Farm Joys
and Labors

THE HARDWOODS glowed against the dark evergreens. The cabin held a fruity smell of wild plums and crabapples. All summer long Mrs. Hill had gathered berries with her children. She had gone on from the first little wild strawberries, sweet as sugar, to the plentiful blueberries and the blackberries.

She made some of the fruits into jams and jellies for the holiday season. Others she canned or dried. The boys shook down butternuts and walnuts, and Alex gathered hazelnuts from the low bushes near the cabin.

"I'll build a path for you through the forest,

Mother," said James. "Then it will be easier for you to gather fruit."

Nearly every day he hacked away at vines and overhanging twigs. Neighbor children joined him, and he played he was manager of a crew of helpers. He was very businesslike and shouted, "Get going! No laggards on my crew."

When September came, James and Mary-Eliza walked with their lunch baskets to school in Rockwood every day. There they joined a dozen other farm and village pupils in the little one-room school taught by Mr. Harris. The teacher was kind but very strict.

Mary-Eliza, who had already been taught many things by her mother, enjoyed history and literature at school. James felt that it was more important to learn spelling and arithmetic.

"I'm going to learn how to figure," he told his sister one day as they walked home from school. "Being a girl, you won't need to know much about figures, but both of us must learn how to spell. Mother says that nothing looks worse in a letter than a misspelled word. Let's spell each other down on our walks."

"I'll always win," Mary-Eliza boasted.

"Maybe," James agreed, "but let me try."

They often saw raccoons in the trees and fox kits playing among the rocks. Squirrels were hiding nuts for the winter.

By this time James and Mary-Eliza had almost forgotten their father's plan to purchase a horse and wagon. Then, one day around Hallowe'en, Mr. Hill drove a mare hitched to a bright wagon through the clearing. The wheels screeched loudly for want of grease. Shep, the collie, let out a sharp bark.

The former owner, Mr. Hill explained, was moving to Toronto to go into business with his brother. James remembered this man, a Mr. Quagmire, as a surly man who squinted when he talked. He had made a special agreement with Mr. Hill, saying, "Pay when you can."

When their father pulled up on the reins in front of the barn, the children ran out to pet the gentle mare. Only Mrs. Hill seemed troubled. James noticed a cloud on her face. "I like the mare but I'm afraid of debt," she said calmly as she stood and looked.

James knew how she felt. His father often had said, "James, you take after your mother in disposition and looks."

James looked at her now. She stood slim, yet she was sturdy. Her neck was a firm column, her nose rather large. Her dark brown hair had golden lights. Her blue Irish eyes reminded him of a shining lake fringed with dark pines. Mr. Hill, lean and fair haired, was well muscled, but he slumped more often than his wife.

Today, however, his voice was strong and joyful. Proudly he unharnessed the mare and led her into the stable he had prepared for her. Her stall was beside that of the cow. The hens, on perches above, cackled.

In lively fashion and in high spirits Mr. Hill ordered his family about. "James, bring in a bucket of oats for Lady here," he said. "Mary-Eliza, bring a pail of water. Alex, stay out from under Lady's feet. You may get an apple or a carrot to feed her. We'll all make her feel welcome to her new home."

"Father!" James exclaimed. "There's a saddle, too. It's here in the back of the wagon. She must be a riding horse."

A little later Mrs. Hill saddled the mare and rode out to the road. She came back flushed with pleasure and said, "James, you're next, and then Mary-Eliza. Maybe I can take Alex with me on my next turn."

In the weeks that followed, Lady became the pet, not only of the family but of the entire countryside. Neighbors came to see and admire her, and children came for short rides. The Hill farm was almost like a circus.

Most of the farmers had work horses, usually Clydesdales, but nobody had a riding horse. Mr. Harris invited James to bring the horse into Rockwood. He gave the boy riding lessons. James learned how to have the little mare trot, lope, and gallop. He even taught her some fancy steps. She learned easily. Perhaps she had been trained before. James realized that his father had indeed obtained a bargain.

One night before Christmas, James woke to hear his father and mother moving about. His father had lighted a lantern and his mother was building up the wood fire. Earlier she had gone out to the barn with a dish of warm mash, but that was not unusual.

By the light of the moon through the window James saw that it was beginning to snow. He

26

shivered out of his bunk and pushed his feet into his moccasins. He pulled on a jacket his mother had made from the best parts of his father's overcoat and hurried to the barn.

The door was ajar. He stepped in, grateful for the moist warmth given off by the horse and the cow. He was glad that he had helped his father chink the cracks in the rough logs with moss to keep out the wind and cold.

Once inside, he pulled the door shut behind him and caught his breath. He stood in wonder gazing at the scene before him. His father and mother were kneeling together joyfully in the stall. Over their shoulders he could see Lady looking down at a golden brown colt.

He pushed forward and reached out timidly to touch the soft, smooth head of the small animal. He made the gesture with such tenderness that neither his father nor his mother reproved him. Lady's eyes shone with pride.

"She has a star on her forehead, like Lady!" James whispered. Then he shouted gleefully, "Hello, Star! That's her name. Star!" He had christened her himself. He felt love for the new-born colt welling up strongly in his body.

Soon the colt struggled to her feet. James laughed aloud as he watched her sprawl out her legs awkwardly. His laughter startled Lady. She let out a loud neigh and reared up. The Hills stepped back.

"It's time for us to leave," Anne Hill said quietly. "Lady will take care of Star."

James took his mother's hand as they walked back to the cabin. "Oh, Mother," he said. "Star is wonderful! I can hardly wait to show her to Mary-Eliza and Alex."

"Son, you sound as if she belonged to you," his father teased, but he sounded pleased.

The colt proved to be a true Christmas gift. Even the fine straight pine that James helped his father cut and drag to the cabin for Christmas could bring no greater joy than the birth of this colt. There was happiness in the house and happiness in the barn! Shep, the collie, nosed the newcomer happily. Tabby, the Maltese cat, played close by and purred. James even stopped by the pigpen to say, "Piggie, you have a new neighbor."

Mary-Eliza strung wild cranberries and popcorn to drape the branches of the Christmas tree. Mother cut out animal cookies. Father brought gay candles from Rockwood and fitted them into holders fastened to the tree.

The Hills invited Mr. Harris, the village schoolteacher, to share their Christmas dinner of browned, baked goose. They rejoiced in the potatoes and corn, the cabbage for making slaw, and the pumpkin for making pies.

Mr. Harris had been a great world traveler, and whenever he spoke, James listened. "I'm going to see the world outside of Rockwood, too," James said. It was more of a promise to himself than a boast.

Another harvest came, and another, before James took his first trip beyond Rockwood. The

Hill family loaded up their produce in the wagon, for a two day trip each way to Toronto. They drove Lady, hitched to the wagon and slept under the wagon at night. Mostly they ate food which they carried with them from home. Once they dined in the marketplace, but the cooking was not as good as home cooking.

The small amount of wheat that they had raised brought twenty cents a bushel. The pork sold for one cent a pound. Mrs. Hill's carefully churned butter sold for ten cents a pound. In all they came home with seven dollars.

Seven silver dollars! Seven dollars in cash! Seven dollars for a season's work! James knew that his father and mother were satisfied, but he felt that somehow life should be easier. Some day he might own a big farm which would enable him to live better. Out there in the world beyond Rockwood there must be great fields, fine cattle, and prosperity.

31

The Terrible
Accident

By HIS NINTH YEAR James Hill had become a sturdy boy, full of life. He was a great help to his father in the fields and in the barn. His father was strict about weekdays and Sundays, but generous about playtime on Saturdays.

On Sundays the family walked or drove to Rockwood to attend the little village church. After a simple Sunday dinner, prepared on Saturday night, the parents read the Gospel and the children learned Psalms.

Later the children changed their Sunday clothes to play clothes. Then they played ball or tramped through the woods.

During one of the happy Saturday vacations, James and Alex made some bows and arrows. In a nearby swamp they found willow sprouts which they easily bent into bows. They made the arrows out of sharpened sticks.

Several boys in the neighborhood met in the woods to play Indian. Shouting and yelling in Indian raid fashion, they scampered in and out among the trees. They shot arrows at a fast rate at knots in the trees which made fine targets for arrows. Little woodland creatures, such as birds, chipmunks, squirrels, raccoons, and rabbits, scurried out of the way.

Suddenly everything changed. There was a scream and the exuberant yelling in the forest shivered into silence. There was a breath-taking stillness in the air.

James Hill with blood streaming down his face ran toward the log cabin, where his mother had just stepped outside. A sobbing boy ran alongside, crying, "I didn't mean to shoot you, James. Honest, I didn't mean to."

Mrs. Hill cried, "No! Oh, no!"

With shaking hands she lifted her son's head. He had been shot by an arrow that lifted his right eyeball out of its socket. Actually he wasn't as frightened as his mother, but he kept sobbing. "It was an accident," he said.

Mrs. Hill screamed for her husband and he came in from the fields. He looked at his son, turned deathly pale, and then composed himself. "Keep him quiet while I go for Dr. MacLeod."

Mrs. Hill saw with horror that the arrow had actually knocked the eyeball from the socket. She tried to think she was only having a nightmare, but she knew better.

She held cold cloths to her son's face. As the cloths turned red, she tried not to let the horror show in her face lest it frighten him still more. Pulling herself together with a supreme effort, she soothed her son and assured him, "Dr. MacLeod will take care of it, son. He'll fix you up, and you'll be all right." **1473738**

The waiting seemed an eternity, but the doctor arrived with Mr. Hill at full speed. His own horse raced beside Lady. He rushed into the cabin with his little black bag.

The moment he came through the door, the terrible tension lifted. Mrs. Hill trusted Dr. MacLeod and knew that he was an expert doctor. He had left a paying practice elsewhere to come here to be of service among pioneers.

The doctor spoke soothingly while he pushed the eyeball back into the socket. With gentle but firm action he skillfully bandaged the eye. "You've been a very brave boy, James," he said. "You're the kind of boy I'd like to train in my office. A steady young man like you would make a great surgeon." He gave the boy a reassuring pat. "Now take care."

"Will he be able to see?" asked Mrs. Hill.

"I hope so," the doctor answered quietly, too quietly to suit Mrs. Hill.

"Tell me once more," she said. "Will he be able to see?"

"I'll know in four weeks," replied the doctor. "At that time I'll remove the bandages and examine the injured eye."

James spent the four weeks helping manfully with the chores. He assured his distraught parents that he could see very well with his left eye. He could even read fine print in the Bible. He was the hero of the neighborhood. He was distinguished by a snowy white bandage. Nobody else had ever had such a fine bandage.

One of his playmates grumbled, "I have never had anything but stone bruises."

"Once I had a big cut in my leg," said another boy, determined to top the first boy. "The doctor put six stitches in my leg."

As usual James ran barefoot, wading in the creeks and playing along the woodland paths. He visited the neighbors. He felt certain that the news at the end of four weeks would be good news. He was so healthy that he had never been sick like other children. The epidemics that put neighbors to bed had passed him by.

The doctor came on the appointed day, but he had nothing to say. He realized that he had come on a serious matter. He did not even ask, "How are you today?" nor did he greet the children. Mrs. Hill sent Mary-Eliza and Alex out to play. Her husband came in and stood beside her, his hands caressing her shoulders.

The doctor seated his patient on a kitchen chair. Carefully he removed the bandages. He pushed back the lid and passed his hands over the eye. The eye was sightless.

He moved his hand once more in front of the eye and turned to give the two anxious parents

the sad report. "The optic nerve has been severed," he explained, "or it may have been severely shocked."

As the two parents stared at him, he added, "I hope that the other eye will stay healthy." He explained that the sight of the other eye might weaken through sympathy. "I have great faith, however, that the lad's health will help him to withstand this ordeal," he said.

A few days later the doctor asked, "James, how would you like to come into my office and let me teach you about my work? I'm sure your father and mother would be pleased. Does Doctor James Hill sound good to you? Would you like to become a doctor?"

James was pleased. He realized that some of the sorrow his mother felt would be eased by the hope that her son would become a doctor.

James worked hard. Every spare moment up to the time he was fourteen, he studied in the doctor's office. At the same time he kept on studying his subjects at school. One book which he studied at the doctor's office was Abernathy's *Anatomy,* from which he memorized many medical terms that doctors need to know. Tibia and fibula became the ABC's of his learning.

The doctor attempted to encourage James by telling him of a famous blind physican who could diagnose by touch alone. James soon recovered from the shock of his loss of sight in one eye. His vigorous health saw him through, as the doctor trusted it might. Most of the time he forgot about the blind eye.

"You're lucky in one way," the doctor said during one of their drives to see a patient in the country. "You'll never have to have that injured eye removed. It is bright and clear, just like your other eye. Even a doctor couldn't tell that it is sightless without looking closely. The only way I can tell that it is sightless is when you turn directly about to face me. Even then the injured eye is hardly noticeable."

"Thank you very much," James said gratefully. "I appreciate what you said because I never want anybody to pity me as a cripple."

"Nonsense!" answered the doctor. "You'll see more with that good left eye than most people see with both eyes."

"Well, I will try!" James commented. "Yes sir-ee! I'll surely try."

One day there was a great flurry in the doctor's office. A man came in carrying a boy who was crying so loudly that James sprang to his feet in terror. He rushed to get the doctor from the next room.

The patient, James was shocked to learn, was the boy who had shot the arrow into his eye. The boy's father explained that he had fallen out of the barn loft while trying to jump with an umbrella like a bird. The umbrella did not hold him up and he had fallen to the hard sand below. Something snapped.

"He has a broken leg," the doctor said. "We'll have to set it, James. You can assist. You've seen the nurse help."

James obeyed the doctor's orders, but it was a painful experience for the boy. He yelled, "You're just trying to hurt me all you can because I shot you in the eye."

James was sweating and miserable by the time the leg was set and in a cast. Even the boy's father was giving him sour glances as if to say, "You're a fine doctor, you are."

Somehow James knew from this experience that he would never be able to earn the name of Doctor James Hill. Instead, he always would be James Hill or maybe just plain Jim Hill.

The Corduroy Road

WHEN JAMES WAS TEN, he made a bargain with his father. He wanted to build a mile of corduroy road across a swampy area on the Hill farm. This road would make the trip to Rockwood safer in the spring and easier in the fall.

"Sinkholes and swamps are dangerous," said James, piling an armload of cordwood outside the kitchen. He was speaking to his father who was sawing cordwood nearby. "One reason it took us so long to go to Toronto was on account of bad roads. I'd like to build a little corduroy road through the woods. You often have said a laborer is worthy of his hire."

"Meaning what?" asked the elder Hill.

"I'd like to build a corduroy road for a price," said James. "I want to earn."

"A price?" asked Mr. Hill. James could see that his father was amused.

"The colt, Father. I'd like to buy Star. I know that Star partly belongs to me because I'm part of the family. But I want to own something all by myself."

"You want to be a young man of property," teased his father. "Well, I'll make a deal. If you build that stretch of corduroy road in six months, I'll give you the colt."

"Do we shake hands on it?" James inquired.

"We shake hands on it," his father agreed and offered his big, workaday hand to his son.

James felt the callouses caused by the tools his father had been handling. Somehow his father always seemed to have a tool in his hands, a maul, a hammer, a scythe, or a rake.

44

James' project was news in the settlement, and neighbor boys flocked to help. Even Alex showed a willingness to tow the small logs to be placed across the bigger logs. Other boys who looked forward to riding the colt came to offer help. The woods rang with the blows of axes and the hatchet slashings of twigs. James measured all the logs and decided where they would be used in building the road.

From time to time his father visited the scene. He would ask, like one businessman to another, "How's the contract coming along? Do you think you'll finish on time?"

James would answer, "Everything's fine—finer than frog's hair." He really felt grown up.

Gradually the new corduroy road attracted great interest in the community. Some of the teenage boys began to help James and some of the older men gave a lift. After all, the road would be used by all the neighbors.

There would be no more driving around sink-holes or skirting the swamp. The whole countryside could cross over to the main road. Reaching Rockwood for supplies would no longer be difficult at any time of the year.

James made certain that everybody kept busy and didn't waste time. Often he would shout to a laggard, "Get a move on, boy, or go home and help your mother." Or he would shout, "Get out of the way, boy. If you don't want to work, don't keep others from working." Sometimes he praised a willing worker by saying, "Take it easy, fellow. That log is bigger than you are. Alex, give the lad a lift."

His best and most effective method was enthusiasm. "Thanks for your help," he'd say. "If we keep on like this, we'll finish the job ahead of time. Then we'll celebrate!"

Getting rid of persons who hindered was as important as encouraging persons who worked.

Some made only pretenses of setting logs into uneven gulches or swampy holes or seas of mud. Some puttered endlessly, never quite finishing what they started and never seeming to know what to do next. Some gossiped, told stories and jokes, and played tag among themselves. Some just stood around and watched.

"Ax leaners are not welcome on this job," James explained. He got rid of the boastful boys who wanted credit for every little thing they did. Either by word or deed they would say, "Look what I did!"

Gradually he built up a steady, hard-working dependable crew. His father said, "Son, you have a good eye for the right workers. If you keep on picking the best helpers, you'll be a success when you're fully grown and go out in the world to make a living."

At the end of six months James had the road finished. "Mother," he announced the first morning at breakfast, "I want you to be the first person to travel over the road."

His mother beamed. "Bring the horse and wagon around," she said to her husband. "I'll be ready in a few minutes."

James hitched Lady to the wagon and led her up to the cabin door. He helped Mrs. Hill climb up to the seat on the wagon where she pulled up the reins. She had put on her Sunday-go-to-meeting dress and her fine felt hat. Also she had put on gloves, which she had never worn before. She was honoring James.

"Go, Lady," she called brightly.

She slapped the reins over Lady's back. The horse trotted briskly into the clearing. At the edge of the unfamiliar corduroy road she halted and reared back. For the first time she balked with the wagon.

"She needs an escort," said James. He stepped jauntily over, took hold of Lady's bridle, and led her onto the corduroy road. Soon the horse found the road safe and was no longer afraid. At the middle of the stretch James jumped aside and Lady went on by herself. Both James and his mother were pleased with the way Lady had traveled on the new road. Both of them glowed with pride.

Soon the colt, Star, came trotting along the road, and James put his arms around her neck. Within a few weeks he would start to ride her to school, but not to the little school that Mr. Harris ran for small children.

A fine, scholarly Quaker, Professor Wetherald, had opened an academy in Rockwood. This new schoolmaster was a handsome, bearded young gentleman who had graduated from colleges of distinction. He was one of the most respected men who had ever come to Rockwood.

Mr. Hill had made all the arrangements for James to enter the academy. He felt that since

James was blind in one eye he would need a good education, the best possible to receive.

For six months James proudly rode Star to school. The academy was housed in a fine old mansion with polished woodwork, marble fireplaces, and rich rugs. A garden walk led up to the front entrance. There were grassy plots at the back for tethering riding horses.

At recess James often let the boys ride Star for short distances. One boy looked with envy at Star and asked whether or not Lady was the colt's mother. James answered that she was, without thinking much about it.

One day the boy's father called for his son in a horse and buggy. James noted that he was Mr. Quagmire who had sold Lady to his father.

The next day the boy wore a strange grin, but James did not worry. He still felt certain that Star was his colt. He had earned her by building the corduroy road.

The happy days flew by. Every morning was a delight. Star welcomed her young master with gambols of joy. She seemed to understand whatever he wanted her to do. He taught her to trot and to canter. He even taught her to do a few fancy high-steps.

All the while that James was happy, he could tell that something was worrying his father. He wondered whether it was something about Star or whether it was something else. Then one frosty morning when he went happily into the barn to saddle Star, he found the stall empty.

Professor
William
Wetherald

FOR ONE AWFUL MOMENT James stared at the empty stall. He could not really believe that his colt was gone. She belonged to him. He had earned her and he had loved her.

He was no cry-baby. Even when his right eye had been shot out by the arrow, the doctor had called him "a very brave boy" but now he wept. Great sobs shook his body. He leaned against the rough feeding trough and caressed the tooth marks that Star had left.

Soon he felt his mother's gentle hand on his shoulders, but she failed to comfort him. She took him in her arms and her tears mingled with his. He still could not stop crying, even though he realized that his display of grief added to her distress.

"Why—why," he finally asked through convulsive sobs, "didn't Father tell me?"

"He was too heartbroken himself," Mrs. Hill explained. "He had offered the Quagmires everything we could spare, but they would not settle for less than the colt herself. Mr. Quagmire himself coveted that colt, and his greedy little son wanted her even more."

Mrs. Hill strove to soothe her son when she felt he was ready to listen, but this was not easy. He was too deeply hurt.

"There's plenty in this world for everyone's needs," she explained, "but not enough for everyone's greeds. The Quagmires are greedy and they must live with their own greedy selves. We Hills, on the other hand, pay our debts, no matter how painful we find the payments to be."

Then she made an odd announcement. "I am driving to Rockwood this morning, and I'll drop you off at the academy. I promised Mrs. Wetherald that I would have breakfast tea with her at her home."

"Do the Wetheralds know about Star?" James asked through his tears.

"Yes, they know," his mother answered. "Your father went to Professor Wetherald as a last resort. The professor tried to persuade the Quagmires to desist in their demands, but without avail. Believe me, we did our best."

When they reached Rockwood, Mrs. Hill went to call on Mrs. Wetherald. The two women drank tea out of delicate china cups and ate scones off dainty plates. James went on to school.

The Quagmire boy rode Star to school and tethered her in the usual place. At noon he offered to let the pupils ride her, but nobody accepted his favor. They played ball.

Thirty school boys lived and boarded in the big old mansion and twelve others came to school during the day. Not a boy in the group accepted an invitation to ride Star. James now realized that he had many fair and loyal friends.

Later, when Professor Wetherald gave him an understanding pat on the shoulder, he felt the hurt in his heart ease a little more. He was very fond of this man and felt that he tried to do what was right.

Soon James began to forgive his father for letting Star go. He remembered the day he had hoped to enter Rockwood Academy and had sat on a bench outside the office door. His father had looked like such a little man, with his gentle chin and a sort of grayness about him. Even though he was small and gentle, he had manifested great earnestness and affection. He had tried to get something important for his son that he had never had for himself.

When James looked at Professor Wetherald, he noted the same kindness on his face that he observed on his father's face. The professor had said, "If thee will study, I have faith thee will enjoy success."

James studied from early spring, when the wolf kits tumbled among the rocks, to deep winter, when grown wolves howled among the frosty trees. As he walked through the woods, he reviewed the facts that he studied at school.

He liked mathematics best of all. With newfound friends he helped the younger boys with their problems. He took a full course in bookkeeping, because someday he might want to keep accounts. He talked over the farm accounts with his father night after night and put to use what he learned in the academy.

"Someday you may handle large sums of money," his father said, as they worked one night at the kitchen table. "Learn to handle small amounts first. Know where every penny goes. Then you can handle big sums."

Everybody at school studied history and literature, as well as mathematics. Often when the pupils took walks with the professor they talked of nature's marvels. Sometimes they discussed books or historical events.

One fine autumn day a friend lent the Hills a copy of Sir Walter Scott's *Ivanhoe.* This was the first book of fiction that James had ever had a chance to read. He enjoyed taking excursions into the magical world of gallant knights and ladies. He was held spellbound by the castles with their moats and drawbridges.

The swordplay and the acts of gallantry were so exciting that he read on by lamplight and then by firelight. Finally his father ordered him to bed. He could hardly sleep for wondering about the outcome of a challenge.

The next morning he started to school early.

He put the book in his knapsack, planning to read a little as he walked to school. It was a brilliant fall day. The hardwoods were glorious with color, and there was a purple mist in the lowlands. The sunlight, pouring down on autumn leaves, created more beauty than the trappings of any knight's horse.

James sat down beside a brook. He intended to read only a chapter or two, but the sun was soon overhead. By this time he was hungry, and he absentmindedly ate his lunch and drank from the brook. Finally when the long shadows fell across the grasses, he came out of his trance. He had spent the day and finished the book.

"I skipped school," he said to himself in astonishment. "I didn't go to school." He was close to tears. Worse still, he was ashamed, but he said nothing at home. He handed the book to Mary-Eliza and said, "Be sure you tend to other things before you start reading."

All night long he tossed and turned. He was sound asleep when his mother shook him awake. He thought the shaking was caused by riders in mail rushing over a trembling bridge.

The hardest thing he had to do was face Professor Wetherald. He arrived at the academy so early that he had to wait for the office to open. His words fairly tumbled over one another as he stammered his confession. He had sat in the woods all day yesterday, he explained, hesitatingly, reading *Ivanhoe.*

"Ivanhoe!" It was plain that the teacher had read *Ivanhoe,* and he did not look shocked or perturbed. He even gave James a smile and a gentle slap on the shoulder as he said, "If thee always wastes thy stolen moments reading good books, thee need never worry."

That morning Professor Wetherald gave James a lesson in Latin, the language spoken by the ancient Romans. Latin often is called a "dead language" because it is no longer spoken by the people in any country, but the Professor made the language live. He pointed out many English words derived from Latin.

"Later on," the professor promised, "I shall teach thee a bit of Greek."

The biggest school event of the year was the spelldown. Pupils came from all the little neighboring country schools to compete in this spelling contest. Even a few adults, including Professor Wetherald, stood in the lineup with the pupils. Many words were pronounced.

Visitors interested in the spellers came from all the small schools round about. Many people from Rockwood also came to the contest. The crowd was so large that the event had to be held in the big room at the town hall.

On the way to the contest Mary-Eliza said to James, "Aren't you glad we studied spelling when we were walking to and from school? I just know you'll win, James. You know every word in the first three books."

"Well I don't know all the words in the world," said James. "I studied a list of words often misspelled by educated people and also a list of unfamiliar words that come from Latin and Greek, but I'm worried."

When they reached the town hall where the contest was to be held, the big room was already crowded. There was a sense of excitement among the onlookers, as well as among the contestants. All the visiting groups were sure that the winner would come from their schools.

Soon the children were lined up in a row and the spelldown began. The crowd, which had been noisy, was suddenly silent. Everyone tried to hear how each word was spelled.

One speller after another went down, often missing a word through nervousness or embarrassment while appearing in public. Each time

there was an audible sigh of disappointment
from different people interested in the pupil.
When there were only a dozen expert spellers
still standing, the excitement was intense.

"Our James Hill is still there," the Rockwood group boasted. They smiled confidently.

Mrs. Hill squeezed her husband's hand. "Of course he can't spell down the master," she whispered, "but I'm right proud of him."

"He's still there," said Mr. Hill quietly.

The spelling words became increasingly difficult. It scarcely seemed possible there were so many hard words in the English language. "We had all the words," Mary-Eliza whispered to Alex. "James and I learned to spell the words in the spelling book. We didn't even know the meanings of many of them."

"Sh!" Alex warned. "The pronouncer has used up all the words in the spelling books. Now he's taken a new list. He hardly knows how to pronounce some of the words himself."

There was a deep silence in the hall. Then chairs scraped as onlookers grew restless. But everybody brightened when Professor Wetherald and James Hill stood alone on the platform. They wondered what would happen.

The professor held up his hand for silence. He put his arm about Jim Hill's shoulder and said, "We'll call the contest a tie. It is not meet that the pupil should spell down the master. I congratulate thee, James Hill, and award thee the prize of a set of books."

"But I didn't spell you down, sir," James cried. "I didn't spell you down."

"Thee could have, son," said Professor Wetherald. "In time thee could."

A New Way
of Life

AFTER THE SPELLDOWN, everyone hurried over
to the old-fashioned inn near the town hall for
refreshments. Men, women, and children enjoyed themselves in the big dining room.

A special baking of thick molasses cookies
had been prepared for the occasion, and the
pitchers had been filled with milk. There were
big pots of tea and coffee for grown-ups.

The old Travis couple who ran the inn were
so clean that everything shone from scrubbings.
They were well known for their housekeeping,
and travelers came out of their way to stop off
at the inn. Since there was no railroad into

the town, the inn was always full of patrons. Back of the inn there was a good stable for taking care of horses. In front there was a row of hitching posts.

Mr. and Mrs. Hill had come to town in their wagon, with Lady pulling the rig. The three children had walked to town. James watched his parents talking seriously with the Travis couple and felt that something was about to happen, but he couldn't tell what. After the three children finished eating, they rushed out into the yard, and started to play. James was still curious and asked Alex and Mary-Eliza, "What's taking place? What's the news?"

"The news is that you won the spelldown," Alex teased, "but something else is in the wind."

"I overheard some of the talk between our parents and the Travises," said Mary-Eliza. "The Travises would like to go to New York State for a year to help their children on a farm. They want our parents to take over the inn while they are gone, partly because of you two strapping boys. They feel that you boys can do all kinds of work around the inn."

James felt a shiver of excitement when he beheld his parents, their heads uplifted, coming to get into the wagon. James helped his mother up to the seat and handed the reins to his father. "Ride here with us, son," said Mr. Hill. "We have much to tell you."

James stood in the wagon box behind his parents, his hands placed on their shoulders for balance. "I'm listening," he said.

Mr. Hill pulled out onto the country road before he replied. "James," he said, his voice trembling slightly, "you are riding with the new managers of the Rockwood Inn."

"Why?" James inquired. "What happened?"

"This came up unexpectedly," his mother said, "but providence provides. The Lord tempers the wind to the shorn lamb. The Travises are going to New York State to help their children on a farm. They want us to take over for a year while they are gone."

"We can still run the farm," his father explained. "We can use many things at the inn which we grow on the farm."

"We can raise all the vegetables," his mother said. "We'll plan to grow what we'll need. Maybe we will have enough berries, too, and nuts for cakes." They talked on and on, as though they could never be thankful enough for this great opportunity. They ended by saying that the spelldown was what had brought them this unexpected good luck.

As they paused to get their breaths, James asked, "How did the spelldown bring this good luck? How could it have anything to do with your taking over the inn?"

"Everything works together for good," Mrs.

Hill quoted happily. "Dear, tell our son how all this good fortune came about."

"To begin with, I think we can thank Professor Wetherald for making the suggestion," his father reasoned. "He knew the Travises were looking for somebody to take over the inn. He pointed out that I know a good deal about raising supplies and that Mother is a good housekeeper. The only thing that kept the fine old couple from asking us was the fact that we have three children who might be dashing in and out and causing a lot of work besides."

Mr. Hill turned to look proudly at his son. "When they saw you at the spelldown tonight, they realized that, instead of being a bother, you would be a help. They'd watched the boys all evening, and might not have noticed you particularly, if you had gone down with the others. Then when you stood up as you did, they saw how big and strong you are."

"And smart," his mother added. She was not given to flattery. She had always said, "Handsome is as handsome does."

"The extra help will come in as needed," his father explained. "The professor wants to talk with you and Alex in the morning. He thinks you can handle the bookkeeping and the billing. Alex can be a bellboy. Mary-Eliza will help with the laundry and bed making."

"Even with all this help, the idea scares us," Mrs. Hill added.

It almost scared James, too, when he stood in front of Professor Wetherald the next morning. Neither he nor Alex had ever dined in a hotel, and both of them were shy.

The professor put them at ease. "Come stand by my desk, James," he said. "We'll pretend my desk is the desk for registering people at the inn, and I enter carrying two pieces of luggage. What do you say to greet me?"

71

"Hello," replied James, but at once he was embarrassed. "I mean, 'Good morning. Good morning, sir. What can I do for you?'" James pretended to offer the professor a pen, assign him a room, and ring the bell.

"Now you come in, Alex," explained the professor. "You are the bellboy. You pick up my luggage and lead the way to my room."

Alex reached for the big suitcase beside the small bag. "Gee whillikins!" he exclaimed. "Is this suitcase filled with rocks?"

"That is not the proper technique," the professor said, laughing. "I have books in that suitcase, but your hotel guest may have tools. Books are heavy, but tools are heavier."

"I apologize, sir," said Alex. "As far as I'm concerned, this suitcase is light as air."

"Don't overdo it," warned the professor. "The principal thing for both of you to remember is that you always should be courteous."

Professor Wetherald kept James all day, showing him special methods of hotel bookkeeping. He showed James how he could make good use of what he had learned in mathematics. He showed him several letter forms and had him write several practice letters. Then he showed him how to make out a hotel bill.

"Running an inn," said the professor, "is a gentleman's business. I'll arrange your schoolwork here so that you'll have proper hours for working at the inn. You'll meet all sorts of people and have to put up with all sorts of conditions. Your life will be enriched by some of the guests, but you'll often find rude and disagreeable ones. In the little back room you'll even see card players and gamblers."

The Hills took over the inn during the busiest season in the fall. Many farmers went through Rockwood with their produce. Traveling salesmen stopped off with their samples and wares on

their way to the cities. The Hill boys were not permitted to miss a day at the academy, but they worked at the hotel during off hours. All day Saturday they toiled on the farm.

There was much more work at the inn than the little family had expected. The boys had to pump water for filling pitchers in the rooms, for cooking and for washing dishes, for laundering, and for filling the horse troughs. Most of this pumping fell to Alex.

"At first I thought I was to be only a bellboy carrying suitcases!" he grumbled. "Now I should have a new title! Water boy."

James fed, curried, and watered the horses in the stable. He took over the desk for registering, kept all the financial records, and made out all the bills for the guests.

The Hills now were happier and more prosperous than they had ever been before. Cash was coming in. Within a few months Mr. Hill had paid off all his debts, including the debt on the farm. As he went over the final accounts with James, he said, "I surely wish I had been this fortunate a few years ago! Then I would never have had to give up Star!"

"Please forget it, Father," James begged. "I have forgotten it."

James offered to take over the night shift, because he was at school most of the day. Besides, he found that he could read and study when he wasn't busy. Sometimes he dozed, but he was always alert to what was going on.

One night there was more activity than usual in the card room. A man who lived in a shabby house at the end of the street was gambling. He had a pair of Clydesdale horses with which he earned his living by hauling produce or moving household goods.

He also had a gentle wife and two fine children, a boy and a girl. They went to the same

Sunday School as the Hill children, and James knew them. His mother often treated them to milk and cake or cookies.

The man kept bidding, even though he was steadily losing. He had already lost all his cash. Soon he offered his house. James stood beside him saying, "Please, sir, don't do that. You can't lose the home for your family."

"Keep out of this," the man growled. He lost again and then he said, "I'm putting up my horses at the turn of a card."

He turned a card. It was the wrong card and he had lost. Then he looked at James and shouted, "You're a jinx. You made me lose."

James was disgusted with the man for his actions and insults, but he led him home through the cold gray dawn, hoping the gamblers would be kind to his family later on. This experience made him vow that when he became an adult, he would never have any part in gambling.

Getting to Know People

THE HILLS ran the Rockwood Inn as a family affair, doing nearly all the work both indoors and out. They were extremely busy, but surprisingly, they found time for visiting.

For one thing, the Hills were very careful planners and workers. Each member of the family had his or her own work to do, and did it well. The work always came first.

James knew and liked a boy named Joseph Fletcher, who formerly had gone to the Harris School, but now went to Rockwood Academy. He had hoped to know the boy better, but Joseph was in a class ahead of James at the academy. Then one winter Joseph's parents went to Europe, and he lived at the inn. He often helped James out at the desk both day and night.

"We have a special name for you," said James one day as the boys chatted at the inn. "Do you know what we call you?"

Joseph answered the question with a laugh. "No, what do you call me?" he asked. "Maybe Joe for short, instead of Joseph."

"We call you Dictionary Fletcher," explained James laughingly. "The name's a compliment because you know so many words."

"I don't know any more words than you do," said Joseph modestly.

"I won't argue," said James.

The Hills always had been familiar with the village stores, the blacksmith shop, and the Quaker meeting house. On the other hand, they had not known many people who lived in the village. Now that they were running the inn, these people were neighbors and business associates. Many of them were helpers.

The people who owned the stores and other business places often sent people to the inn. One morning the blacksmith sent over a man who said, "The smithy, who is shoeing my horse, suggested that I come here for breakfast. He said that I could be eating while I am waiting. Please prepare me a big hearty breakfast of pancakes with real maple syrup. Also I should like to have several slices of that tasty bacon for which you are noted."

While the stranger ate his buckwheat cakes and bacon, he told James about the great steamers on the Mississippi River. "A husky boy like you should go west," he advised enthusiastically. "There is plenty of work there for boys."

There was a carpenter and sort of plumber in the village, named North. From time to time Mr. North came to make repairs at the inn.

Some years before, he had helped to build the Rockwood Academy, a fine, three-story building with big chimneys. The front wall had ornate decorations that people called "gingerbread."

"I like nice, carved decorations on a house the way I like frosting on a cake," he confessed. "Fancy work on a house is just as beautiful as lace and ruffles on a lady's dress."

He went on to describe the new school being started by the Misses Harris, half-sisters of John Harris. "It would be nice," he said, "if your sister, Mary-Eliza, could study with these ladies. She could learn to play the piano or organ and to do embroidery."

"There is running water in the academy," said James. "Did you help to pipe it in?"

"Yes, that was practically my job," said Mr. North. "You could have running water at the inn with very little work, simply by piping water from the spring on the hillside."

"Let's talk the matter over with Father and then get busy," James said enthusiastically. "I'll help you, Mr. North, free of charge, just to learn what you can teach me. I know that will be plenty, and it will all be useful."

"That will be plenty," Mr. North agreed, and the project was under way.

James worked for several weeks with Mr. North to prepare pipes for bringing water from the spring to the inn. At last the work was completed and both the Hills and their guests were very happy.

In the meantime Mary-Eliza signed up for a lesson a week with the Misses Harris, but she never failed to help her mother with the beds. She carried up pitchers of warm water every morning so that guests wouldn't have to use the cold water standing in the pitchers. She changed the towels and washcloths and put pink bars of soap in the soap dishes.

Alex emptied the soiled water and the cigar ashes and the waste baskets. This was a big job when all the rooms were filled.

Mrs. Hill planned the meals for the dining room and did much of the cooking. Visitors always carried away memories of her chicken pot pie, her pot roast with dumplings, her roast beef with pan pudding, her potato pancakes, her pies, and her cookies.

There were several churches in town, but the most prominent was the Quaker Meeting House. John Harris and many other important persons in town were Quakers. They had come here when the country was a wilderness filled with wolves, bears, and other wild animals.

All had cut down trees and built homes, just as the Hills had done. There were few roads and no railroads. Thus people who came to the inn often stayed for days at a time.

Most of the pioneers were God-fearing, devout Christians. When newcomers questioned the teaching of the Bible in the schools, the Hills were shocked. They felt that persons should read the Gospel daily and couldn't understand why the newcomers objected. Finally it was decided that the school could teach the Bible to children whose parents requested it.

Even in the midst of his busy life, Mr. Hill took time on Sunday evenings to recite poems and to play the flute. Often he sang one of Robert Burns' poems set to music or he sang the accompaniment to Mary-Eliza's simple organ tunes. Now and then neighbors gathered to hear him sing.

James always remembered one particular evening when his father sang one of the Bobbie Burns' love songs to his mother.

> "My luv is like a red, red rose
>   That's lately sprung in June;
> My luv is like a melody
>   That's sweetly played in tune."

Both parents worked tirelessly for their children, and the children in turn worked tirelessly for their parents. James often thought how thankful he should be for his home and a closely knit, well organized family.

Often late at night James heard the rumble of his father's farm wagon driving in with produce for the inn. He brought vegetables and melons in season and wild hay for the stables. Often Mrs. Hill said to him, "Remember, you cannot do the work of two men."

Mr. Hill tried to maintain good spirits, but he had problems. He could run the inn properly, but he couldn't manage all the work on the farm. James and Alex realized this and offered to quit Rockwood Academy in order to help more.

"No!" their father stated firmly. "Education can change a man's life. I do not know how long I can be on the firing line for my sons. Right now I can give you your chance to attain valuable knowledge. I can give my daughter music lessons. The time for me to work hard is now, while I can help you. If you give me your spare time and your Saturdays, I'll manage. You must get an education while you can. Don't even think about leaving school."

Mr. Hill was ambitious, but both boys feared he was failing in health. He was becoming thin, and his pale cheeks often were sunken and flushed. Lines appeared in his face, and sometimes he stumbled when he hurried.

Their mother seemed to blossom in the busy atmosphere. She was stimulated rather than exhausted by her endless cooking and washing. As Christmas neared she turned out endless batches of cookies. Her fruitcakes made the whole inn seem spicy and sweet.

James went out with his father to cut down an evergreen for the lobby and a smaller tree for the family parlor. Together they chose a tall,

shapely spruce for the lobby of the inn and a
small fir for the parlor.

On this occasion, for the first time, Mr. Hill
made no effort to help cut the trees. James

dragged the trees into the wagon box by himself and settled down to hold them. His father rested with his body slumped over on the wagon seat, waiting to drive Lady home.

"I'm getting lazy in my old age," he apologized. "The time will come when you'll have to take over as the man of the house."

Then he began to whistle softly as the wagon turned onto the road. It was a tuneless whistle, a classic whistle with lovely words. "My luv is like a red, red rose."

Christmas Day, 1852

ALL THE AUTUMN labors had been slanted towards Christmas. As James and Alex helped their father gather the farm crops, including corn, potatoes, rutabagas, and late apples, they grew ruddy with health.

By the time the snow fell, they had shocked and shucked the corn. They had stored an ample supply of root vegetables in clean sand in the basement of the inn.

These harvesting activities, as the maple leaves changed to red and gold and fluttered down from the trees, held a glory and a promise. Everything was ready for the long winter.

The patrons at the inn were highly pleased with the services at the inn and kept coming back. All the while the Hills kept on working as hard as ever, even with the new pipes that brought in running water.

James kept careful accounts. One day, a week before Christmas, he bent over the books with his father and pointed out the profits. He was proud to hear his father say, "Son, the farm now belongs to the family, lock, stock, and barrel. The land is ours with all the buildings, such as they are. You are my eldest son, and when the time comes, I'll hand it over to you. I have great faith that you will be able to become the head of the house."

It seemed very strange for Mr. Hill to talk in this manner. It was almost as if he were making a speech that he had rehearsed beforehand. For some queer reason the words made James feel a lump in his throat.

90

On Christmas Eve the family went to the little church next to the inn to celebrate the birth of Christ. With childlike faith they listened to the Gospel story of Jesus. They heard again the tale of the babe, born in a stable because there was no room for Mary and Joseph at the inn. James thought, "There will always be room for any wayfarer at our inn."

As the Hills walked home, great feathery snowflakes were falling from the starlit sky. Professor Wetherald had pointed out that each flake was quite different from every other flake. James had examined a few flakes under a microscope and thought that the intricate crystals were as lovely as the jewels in a necklace.

Professor Wetherald and his wife had invited the Hills to the Rockwood Academy for breakfast on Christmas morning. All the students at the academy were on holiday vacation.

As James assisted his mother up the wide

stone steps between the posts under the delicately carved Romanesque front door arch, he felt a sense of belonging. This was his school, and he was proud of it, even the mahogany paneled hall of the building. The tiled fireplace in the dining room blazed with golden blue flames. Sunlight glistened through the thick glass window panes, framed by rich velvet drapes.

"I have spent my happiest years in this grand house," James said to his mother. "I wish I could stay on and on."

"Why not?" his mother asked. "Your father and I want you to have a fine education."

They sat down to a bountiful breakfast. From one person to another they passed the eggs, the spiced ham, the tasty scones, the rich jam, and the great silver bowl of fruit. The professor himself served as butler.

Mrs. Hill, who had always waited on others, had never enjoyed such service. She was gay and very much relaxed. She was appreciative of her special day of freedom from work and responsibility. Turning to her husband, she said gayly, "I always said I could enjoy luxury."

"It was always your right," Mr. Hill replied gallantly, "even though you never had it."

"But she will," James put in.

His father's smile was warm but wistful. He did not eat with the hearty appetite of the others. When the fruit was passed, he merely took an orange from the tray. He rubbed the smooth peel of the orange and sniffed its fragrance. Then he slowly peeled it with the silver fruit knife, tasted it, and said, "Now I am enjoying luxury."

Later he had a spell of coughing, and Mrs. Hill showed concern. She looked at him as if to ask, "Don't you feel well, James?" But she knew he would not want her to speak out.

At the Rockwood Inn at noon the great family

table was spread with a fine linen tablecloth from Ireland. There were silver candlesticks, which were cherished heirlooms. The centerpiece included polished apples and frosty-blue ground-pine and pine cones.

The table fairly groaned, as the villagers would have said. Mr. Hill sat at the head to carve the turkey, and Mrs. Hill sat at the foot, where she would be able to serve steamed pudding from a huge silver platter. The air was filled with delectable odors.

Long before Mr. Hill had finished carving, the Travis cook came in and offered to take over. With trembling hands Mr. Hill turned over the carving set, and the cook said, "Thank you, sir, for permitting me to have a share in this wonderful Christmas celebration."

Mr. Hill kept on smiling and urging everybody to eat well, but he ate very little himself. Once when Mrs. Hill looked up with a questioning

glance, he said, "The chutney this year is especially good."

There were few guests at the hotel on Christmas, and they were careful to keep off by themselves. They did not want to disturb the Hills and keep them from having a wonderful time.

Later everybody gathered in the parlor, where the Christmas tree had been placed. The tree had been decorated with ornaments saved over the years. Every bright glass ornament, especially the angel with glittery wings at the top, and every bit of tinsel on the tree brought back memories of former Christmas seasons.

Mary-Eliza had strung popcorn and cranberries to loop the branches. Mother had made popcorn balls, cut animal cookies, and gilded nuts to enhance the beauty of the tree.

The Hill children carefully lit the candles set in tin holders attached to the tree and admired the results of their efforts. Mrs. Hill handed out the gifts—the shirts, the dressgoods, the pens and pencils, and the boxes of writing paper. There was a great glow of satisfaction in her eyes.

The Harris sisters came in to play and sing Christmas carols, and the Hills joined them in singing. Throughout the evening the Inn seemed to be filled with a special kind of joy, such as only Christmas could bring.

James was the only person who noticed Mr. Hill slip out of the room. He felt a strange uneasiness come over him as he watched his father leave, quiet as a shadow. He knew that his father had a severe cold, but somehow he sensed an alarming situation.

As quietly as his father had slipped out, he left the singing group. The beautiful words "Silent Night, Holy Night" followed him down the hall. He paused for a moment in the doorway of the master bedroom where his father and mother slept. His father had lain down, fully clothed, on the familiar patchwork quilt which the family had used for many years.

James went forward and looked down, asking, "Father, are you all right?"

There was no answer, and James understood full well what had happened. Briefly he stood with bowed head, realizing that now as the oldest son, he was head of the family.

Later, as an adult, James often said that he had wept only two times in his life. The first time was when he found the stable empty after he had built the corduroy road in order to obtain Star. The second time was at the death of his hard-working father, who had grubbed all his life for the welfare of his children.

Head of the Family

MR. HILL's DEATH left the members of his family desolate, but they had to carry on. Mrs. Hill sat down to discuss the situation with James. "Your father always said that he wanted to die like Bobbie Burns, owing no man, and he achieved this desire," she said.

"The farm is free of debt," she went on. "We can manage to make a good living. My only regret is that you will have to leave school. I'm sorry about that."

"Don't worry, Mother," said James. "I'll do my best to take my obligations in the way Father would have wanted me to."

"As head of the family, you will have great responsibilities, and I wish you could have had a few more years in school," said his mother. "However, your best is good enough for me."

"We must get our plans for the future under way," said James, although there was a lump in his throat. "We must carry on."

"Your father wouldn't want us to dawdle," Mrs. Hill agreed. "Go look over your father's will, which is at the academy where he made it and had it witnessed. Professor Wetherald wants to talk with you, anyway. He will give you good advice, and he may be of some comfort."

Soon young James Hill sat opposite Professor Wetherald in the familiar study of Rockwood Academy. Between them was the big, shiny surface of the polished rosewood desk. Today it had been cleared of all papers except the will.

Professor Wetherald did not speak about the will at once. Instead he said, "James, I have taught you three important things, to concentrate, to reason, and to remember. Your father has taught you something even more important —how to apply the things I have taught you."

"Yes, sir." James swallowed hard.

"Your father has taught you how to work hard and successfully," the professor continued. "He has shown you how to work diligently and well. You have a fine heritage."

"I realize that, sir," said James.

"It is natural for you to mourn your father's death," Professor Wetherald went on. "But I want to read you something from Thomas Carlyle that I hope won't be over your head."

"I'll try, sir," James said thoughtfully. "With the help of your teaching, I'll do my best to understand."

"Thomas Carlyle once said, 'Death is the most joyfullest thing in life when it transfers responsibility to those big enough to shoulder it, for that's the only way you can become a man,' " the professor quoted.

There was a long silence in the room. James sat up straighter in his chair and Professor Wetherald took a long breath. "You're no longer a boy, James," he said. "You're a man."

"I'll have to quit school," James reminded his teacher. "I wish I could stay."

"No man ever quits school!" the professor said, gently striking the top of the desk. "Instead he goes to school all his life. He continues to learn in a store, a shop, a factory, or on a farm, as well as in an academy."

"Oh, I'm going to keep on reading and learning all I can in other ways," James assured his teacher. "I only wish I could keep on studying at the academy."

The professor's voice was lower and more mellow now. "Right now, James, you own a farm that it took your father a lifetime to develop.

First he had to cut timber and build a log cabin. He had to lay out fields and plant an orchard. At times he had to borrow money to tide him over so that all of you could be fed and clothed. At last he managed to pay off the mortgage on the farm. Now the farm free from debt is yours, and you face a great responsibility."

James heard the words of the will in a daze. As the oldest son of his father, he was now head of the family. He was heir to his father's estate, which consisted of the farm. With this inheritance went the responsibility of taking care of the entire family.

"I feel sort of proud," he said, catching his breath as though he had been running, "and sort of scared at the same time."

"Well, being sort of proud and sort of scared at the same time," said his teacher, "you're pretty apt to keep your feet on the ground. I have the utmost confidence in you."

The Hills learned that Mr. Hill had made out his will only two weeks before his death. He had also purchased the family plot in the little church cemetery where he was buried. He had always said he wanted to leave his house in order. Now the family understood his contented smile during the Christmas holiday. He realized that he had to leave the members of his family whom he loved, but he had everything in order.

The death of Mr. Hill completely changed the lives of Mrs. Hill and the children. From then on, they found the work of the inn tedious. They knew that Mr. Hill had worked hard, but they hadn't realized how much he had really done. Now Mrs. Hill had to take over purchasing supplies, which took up much of her time. The boys had to spend much of their time cutting wood and stoking the stoves at the inn.

Towards spring some newcomers came to the inn, hoping to settle nearby. A young Englishman who signed the register "Rolf Harris" remarked, "I understand this part of Canada is mighty cold and dangerous in winter. They say milk freezes before it reaches the pail and that the country is full of bears and wolves."

"Then why did you come, sir?" asked James.

"Adventure," the young man answered. "I'm a Quaker, and I heard about this place back in England, when it was called Brotherstown. It was settled by Quakers, I understand. They probably were a sturdy lot."

"They were indeed," James assured the stranger. "John Harris, possibly an ancester of yours, founded Brotherstown with William Smith. Later the name was changed to Rockwood. The Harris family lived in a log house and Mrs. Harris taught school in one room of her house. She had boarding pupils, but we children walked over from our farm. Finally, when I was about nine years old, the house burned down."

"I've heard about the fire. There was a story about it in the papers. How did it happen?"

"It was a cold night and someone stuffed the school stove full of cedar wood," James explained. "Cedar, as you know, makes a very hot fire. The burning wood overheated a stovepipe that passed through a floor and ignited the floor. Soon the whole house was on fire with flames shooting upward. We could see the flames and billowing smoke from our farm."

"Did anyone die?" asked Mr. Harris.

"There were about thirty people in the house, including the family and the boarding pupils," replied James. "All of them were saved. Then all the neighbors round about cut down trees and rebuilt the house in fourteen days."

"What did the children do in the meantime?" asked Mr. Harris. "Did they want the school to be rebuilt?"

"They certainly did," replied James. "They

loved their school and kept right on meeting and studying in a house a short distance away. They did not miss a single lesson."

"That's typical of Quakers and their method and order of living," observed Harris.

"It is typical of all pioneer settlers," James said. "When my own father came here in 1829 with his parents, this was a true wilderness. In 1833 he married Ann Dunbar and had fifty acres of forest from which to earn a living. He was a brave, hard-working man, with faith in God like all the other settlers."

Then James hesitated and added, "He died just this past Christmas. I'm sure, however, if he were here, that he'd advise you to settle in this part of the country with us."

"I'll try Toronto first," Harris decided. "Most persons who come here to settle are handicapped in finding work. There isn't much of anything for them to do except to cut lumber or dig post-

holes for the Grand Trunk Railway. I'll try something else."

The young Quaker looked at James and continued to talk, "I have itching heels. You may not know what that means. Maybe you'll be content to stay here all your life."

"Maybe I won't," said James with spirit. "Maybe I'll get itching heels, too."

After a time the Travis couple decided to return to Rockwood and once more take over the Rockwood Inn. The old couple paid Mrs. Hill for the pipes which James and others had installed to bring running water to the inn. Now she and the other members of the family sadly began to pack their belongings to go back to the old log cabin on the farm.

As Mrs. Hill folded a patchwork quilt, she said, "James, we may feel rewarded for all the work we have done here at the inn. We leave with the satisfaction of knowing that the inn is in far better condition than it was when we came. Also we have built up the trade."

Back on the farm, the Hills cultivated and planted their fields and garden. They raised chickens and purchased a milk cow. They made necessary repairs to the house.

James and Alex no longer attended the Rockwood Academy, nor did Mary-Eliza take lessons with the Misses Harris. They worked hard throughout the day, but managed to find time to read books from the family bookshelf during the evenings. They had saved some books at the inn.

Mary-Eliza learned to pick out a few tunes on her father's flute. In a proud moment she played "My Luv Is Like a Red, Red Rose," but she never could play as well as her father.

Finally Professor Wetherald recommended James for a job at the village store. His job, as he described it, was to sell calico, sugar, and kerosene to the customers. Also he helped with the mail in the postoffice in the store.

"The Professor gave you a strong recommendation," the owner of the store said to James. "He said that I would make no mistake in hiring you for the job. He pointed out your aptitude in mathematics and your ability in keeping accounts. He called attention to your genial disposition which should make you a good clerk."

The pay was a dollar a week. James arrived early to sweep out the store or build the fire. He loaded and unloaded produce and waited on customers. He was happy to be able to earn even small pay on a job. Somehow he felt that he was beginning to live up to his father's expectations and fond hopes.

Usually he walked to work. However, on the days when his mother had eggs or butter to sell, he drove Lady to the store. He grew almost as fond of Lady as he had been of Star.

Before the end of the year, the owner of the store increased James' salary to three dollars a week. On the strength of his raise, Mrs. Hill decided to move her family to Rockwood, and rented a small house down the street from the store. She hoped that all members of the family would secure work and that they could keep on running the farm.

The family made many plans for their new way of living. They decided to take Lady and the cow with them, and to continue to plant and reap crops on the farm.

In town the family found more time for enjoyment. The children attended parties and continued to read and study. Every few days Professor Wetherald stopped at the store to bring a book or two to James.

At this time many immigrants were coming to Canada from Scotland and Ireland. Some had a hard time learning to speak and write English. James often helped to tutor them, and they, in turn, taught him their languages.

Professor Wetherald lent James several historical books and books of poems to read. Some of these books told how Napoleon Bonaparte had risen to power in France and had conquered much of Europe. While reading about Bonaparte's family, James discovered the name Jerome, which he liked, and decided to use it for a middle name. From this time on he always wrote his name as James J. Hill.

James was happy working in the store, but he missed his Saturday walks with Professor Wetherald. Often they had discussed religious education and its value. James determined that, should he ever have enough money, he would assist churches in founding and managing colleges and other schools.

From his study of Napoleon and other famous persons, he deducted an important philosophy of life. He firmly believed that when a person decided to accomplish something, he had won half the battle. This also was the philosophy of Professor Wetherald who advised his students, "Get started and the rest will come."

Every year an historical panorama was presented in Rockwood. This panorama consisted of a long roll or reel of pictures which gave the highlights of an important historical event. Usually Napoleon's battles were part of it.

The panorama furnished instruction as well as entertainment and was widely attended. An assistant turned the reel to show the pictures, and a lecturer gave an interesting lecture, explaining the action in the pictures.

Now that James lived in town, he wanted to help with the panorama. He stood about in the hall, waiting for a chance to talk to the man in charge. Finally he told the man what he wanted and made a good impression. The man gave him the job of running the picture reel. Also he handed him free tickets for the Hill family.

James found the job interesting at first, but he soon became bored from seeing the same pictures over and over. One night when he was dreamily showing the pictures, the audience broke into uncontrollable laughter. Then suddenly the manager rushed into the cubicle where James worked, shouting, "You Dummkopf!"

James had been showing pictures of cavalry reinforcements arriving to save a battle. In showing the picture, he had reversed the reel, causing the horses to come backing in, tails first. This was a dreadful mistake, and he didn't even wait to be fired.

Anne and Alex and most of the audience laughed, but his mother did not think the incident was funny. She wasn't the type to jest about anything that involved failures.

Boy with Itching Heels

As HEAD OF THE FAMILY, James was a hard worker like his father, but he had one great advantage. He was much healthier and stronger than his father, and he could endure more rigorous work. He felt that no task was too great to undertake or complete. Even chopping wood or cutting corn seemed almost like play.

Now for the first time in his life James began to feel bored. His work at the store brought few changes from day to day, and he became restless. He wondered whether this kind of life would go on forever. It was pleasant enough, but he had itching heels.

116

At mealtime he talked mostly of travelers he met in the store. Often these men told exciting stories of adventure, which his mother called "tall tales."

"There was a fellow in the store today," James said at home, "who once hopped a freighter on the way to China. You should have heard him tell about Hong Kong, the British Crown Colony. The people there are becoming rich from selling shipments of spice, cleverly embroidered silks, and beautiful hand-painted fans."

"Why," Mary-Eliza would ask, "do you want to go to China and eat rice?"

Every once in a while families passed through Rockwood, moving West. Many were on their way to California to seek gold. James often listened to their plans and wondered whether or not he should consider going, too. Then, he could hop a freighter, as the fellow said, from the west coast across the Pacific to China.

One morning at breakfast, Alex teased, "What wild tales do you expect to hear at the store today? I suppose you'll come home tonight talking about the fine things to see and do in faraway New Guinea and Madagascar. Then you'll want to take off and go there."

Ever since his father's death James had felt that he was more or less responsible for looking after his mother and brother and sister. "I wouldn't think of leaving you, Mother, as long as you need me," he frequently said.

He glanced at Alex, who was eating his porridge. "Alex is older than I was when I took the job at the store. Now he is almost sixteen, and I'm going on seventeen. I hope that sometime I can find something else to do. I don't always want to be a clerk in a store."

"You won't be," said his mother.

"Maybe I'll never get any farther from home than Toronto," James continued.

118

"That's only fifty miles," said his mother. "You could walk farther than that."

James was always very careful not to worry his mother, but he noticed that she watched him closely at sociables, parties, and barn dances. She seemed to be particularly concerned when he listened spellbound to strangers, telling exciting tales of adventure and travel.

"There are lots worse places than Rockwood," Mary-Eliza said to her mother as they sat pulling basting threads. The two of them did quite a bit of sewing for neighbors. "We're much better off than we were when we lived on the farm. All of us can work here and we're prosperous, aren't we? I know we work hard, washing, ironing, sewing, and tending crops at the farm. James also works hard at the store, but he would have to work hard anywhere else."

"It's rewarding work he wants," Mrs. Hill explained. "He wants advancement!"

One evening Alex came home after helping to deliver groceries from the store. "I reminded James that it was supper time," he said, "but he is talking with a stranger. This man is telling him about steamboats on the Mississippi River over in the States."

As Alex hung up his coat, he continued, "This man is leading James to believe that people over there are looking everywhere for strong young fellows to work as roustabouts. I'm really worried about James. Sometimes I fear that he is riding downhill without any brakes."

Mrs. Hill raised her stubborn chin. "I've seen this coming for a long time," she said, "but I do not intend to apply the brakes."

No one in the family was surprised when James burst in with wild talk about leaving Rockwood and going south before winter set in. Then he could get a job with a man named Kittson, who would be on his way North with a dog

120

team to buy furs from the Indians. The wages were always good for the work.

James scarcely seemed to know what he was eating. The stew was well flavored and the biscuits were hot, but he ate thoughtlessly. He completely ignored his favorite pickled crabapples, which filled a center dish on the table.

"I still want to hop a freighter going to China," he confided, avoiding Mary-Eliza's eyes. "This job with Kittson will tide me over until I can move on to the Pacific coast."

He spread the butter thick on his split biscuit. "What do you say, Mother? Alex is old enough to take over my place in the family and take over my job in the store. I've already talked with the man at the store and he says he'll be glad to hire Alex in my place."

Everyone laughed. "It looks as if you've already decided everything," cried Alex. "From now on I'm the man of the house!"

"James has decided." Mrs. Hill looked at her son, her eyes shining with pride and affection. "Man is a migrating animal. He vegetates if he stays in one place and sits still."

James jumped to his feet and gave his mother a resounding kiss. Then he settled back to enjoy the dish of bread pudding, savory with spices, that Mary-Eliza brought to the table.

As Mrs. Hill passed the pitcher of cream, he said gaily, "I'll bet they won't have bread pudding like this at Pig's Eye."

"Pig's Eye!" the others exclaimed.

"Yes, Pig's Eye!" said James. "It sounds strange but it's a real place on the Mississippi River in a territory called Minnesota, over in the States somewhere."

Mrs. Hill wanted to give James all the encouragement she could. "Have faith in your dreams, son," she said approvingly. "They can become realities. And enjoy your adventures."

She offered James twenty dollars, which she had managed to save out of his wages and her own poorly paid sewing. She insisted that he take the money for safety.

"When should I plan to go?" he asked.

"Go now!" she answered, to his astonishment.

"But can you spare the money?" he asked.

Mrs. Hill's eyes shone brightly as she said, "The Hills have never gone hungry and never will. When we harvest the crops from the farm, we will have all we need for our own use and some left over to sell. Also we can pick some wild grapes and other fruits for jelly."

James found it especially hard to bid good-by to Professor Wetherald. From time to time the professor had lent him travel books and story books about countries all over the world. He had encouraged him to become interested in foreign places and seemed to understand his burning desire for travel and adventure.

Professor Wetherald had particularly advised James to look into opportunities in the States. "Sometimes," he said, "happiness and adventure can be found next door."

The evening before James departed, Mrs. Hill pressed and mended his clothes. "A young man should have an opportunity to find a place in the world before he settles down with a family," she said. "You were fortunate to be able to work at the store, but now that you're going on seventeen, it's time to do something bigger and better. From now on, as you know, you won't have to worry about us."

"Yes, I know," James said seriously. "I'll send you money once in a while. And someday I'll come back with enough money to give you all the things Father wanted to give you."

"I know you will," Mrs. Hill agreed.

Before daylight the next morning, James tied his bundle of clothes and a package of food

to a stout, straight stick which he could carry over his shoulder. He ate a hearty breakfast which his mother had prepared. He shook hands with Alex and gave Mary-Eliza a kiss and a brotherly hug. He kissed his mother tenderly and she gave him her blessing. Then solemnly she stood back, straight and tall.

At the break of day he put the stick over his shoulder and started walking. He waved back several times as the members of the family watched. Only when he saw his mother turn to pull weeds in the flowers did he quicken his pace.

The last thing he heard from them was Mary-Eliza's bright, bird-like voice. "Look, Mother! Look, Alex! James is walking away fast as if he has itching heels."

Chuckling, James said to himself, "How right she is! I do have itching heels!"

To the Jumping-off Place

To CONSERVE his twenty dollars in cash, James had decided to walk to Toronto. It was only fifty miles away. He wouldn't be much of a traveler if he couldn't walk fifty miles.

With the packet of his mother's good cooking he would not have to stop to buy food. All he would need for several days would be an occasional drink from a spring or a brook.

When he reached Toronto, he remembered his mother's admonition; "Keep going. Now is the time." He went to the wharf and bought a ticket on a leaky old steamboat to Niagara. The boat was so old that he wondered whether he would even get there. He arrived safely, however, and walked on to Buffalo.

The city of Buffalo was filled with hustle and bustle, both night and day. The streets were crowded with immigrants, waiting to board boats to travel westward over the Great Lakes. James went down to the wharves and found that he could obtain work on a schooner bound for Chicago. Here was his chance to go west.

The pay was meager, but he would have board and lodging during the ten days it would take the schooner to reach Chicago. His chief interest was to travel the greatest possible distance in the least possible time.

When the schooner reached Chicago, he immediately looked for a job. To his surprise he obtained work as assistant to a freight official. He would help to keep records and his pay would be a dollar a day.

"If Mother could see me now!" he chuckled.

128

"My first job back in Rockwood was a dollar a week. Here, on my first job out in the world, I'll earn a dollar a day."

The freight official said, "You may not be able to figure, but with those muscles, you surely ought to be able to lift."

How Professor Wetherald would have laughed at that remark! He had often boasted about his pupil's skill in mathematics. Now the pupil had an opportunity to prove himself.

Proudly James sent his mother twenty dollars. He informed her that he was already prosperous. Earning money was just a game.

Soon James left the freight job and joined a party bound for California on a wagon train. When he reached Rock Island, he noticed a sign on a sawmill which read, "Man wanted." He applied for a job and obtained work in the accounting department. He enjoyed the work because it enabled him to use mathematics.

James soon became restless and decided to move on. He remembered his mother's remark, "Man is a migrating animal." This certainly seemed to apply to him.

Soon he went to Davenport, where he first caught a glimpse of the Mississippi River. He thought that the steamboats on the river were the most beautiful things he had ever seen in his life. Back in Rockwood he had heard of side-wheelers and sternwheelers, but nobody had ever fully described their beauty.

Once evening at dusk he attended a celebration to greet one of the luxurious queens of the river. Like a majestic white swan she moved in with graceful slowness. She was like a great lady, taking her time to make an entrance. The country boy gaped in wonder.

The smokestack belched fire, but he was entranced by the fairy-like decks of the superstructure. Gold letters on the white pilot house proudly proclaimed her name to the public. If only Mary-Eliza could see her!

As the gangplank was let down, he heard the mellow voices of the deckhands singing. In a few moments the captain came out of the pilot house. He was an impressive bearded man in an immaculate blue uniform with gold buttons and gold braid. He came down to the lower deck and walked proudly ashore.

The people who followed him looked important and prosperous. The women wore fashionable clothes and had plumes in their hats. The men wore neatly tailored suits and tall silk hats. Everybody seemed to be carefree and happy.

Time after time James went to the wharf to watch incoming steamboats. He was fascinated both by the boats and the passengers on the boats. More and more he became anxious to experience the pleasure of riding on a boat.

On impulse he bought a ticket on the "Molly

Divine" for a few days' outing. He never imagined that people could live and travel in such luxury. He slept in a stateroom between sheets that felt as fine as silk. He dined at tables spread with immaculate white linens and used napkins as large as small tablecloths.

He ate with silver utensils, including forks of shapes and sizes that he had never seen before. He drank from sparkling crystal cups and sniffed odorous flowers. All the while he wondered what the members of his family would think if they could see him now.

The short time James spent in this atmosphere was quite enough to satisfy his curiosity. "What I spent on this trip for a few days' luxury would feed a large family for a month," he said to himself. "Besides, Mother's cooking is just as good as the chef's."

When he left the boat back in Davenport, he went straight to the office of the steamboat company to ask for a job. He was sure that he wanted to work for a steamboat company. Fortunately the man in the office said that he could use a shipping clerk.

Now James had free passage on all the company boats. In the late fall he decided to take a trip northward to the end of the line. Soon the river would be frozen and the boats would stop running. The company would have no further use for his services until the spring thaw, several months later.

The town at the end of the line was called Pig's Eye. This was the place the traveling salesman back in Rockwood had told him about. According to the salesman, the town needed roustabouts, and he planned to stop there, work a while, and then go on to California. From there he probably could go on to China.

When James reached Pig's Eye, he found it a nice little river town, even though it had an unsavory name. The main part of the village was quite level, but it was encircled by hills. Nearby there was an Indian village. Many people milled about the wharf to watch passengers come down the gangpank from the boat.

"It's too bad you didn't arrive a few days ago," said a friendly villager. "You missed the concert by Ole Bull, the famous violinist. And last night you missed hearing Adelina Patti, the beautiful soloist. We had to turn crowds away from both of these performances. This may be a wilderness, but we folks who live here certainly appreciate culture."

James knew that his mother and Professor Wetherald would have enjoyed those great artists, but right now he was chiefly interested in something else. "I'm eager to meet a man here named Kittson who travels northward," he said to a villager. "Can you tell me when he will be ready to start North with his oxcarts?"

"Mr. Kittson has been gone for some time," the man answered. "He went North several weeks ago and won't return until spring."

"I seem to be on the missing end of things," James complained. "Maybe I can get a job here for a few weeks and then move on."

Every hotel, boardinghouse, and rooming house was full to overflowing. Men stood in line to get into restaurants. The very air about the town was full of hope and enthusiasm. James liked the lively spirit of the place.

He had sent his last earnings home. "I'm penniless here among strangers," he thought. Then he remembered the words of the stranger in Rockwood, "What wouldn't they give at Pig's Eye for a good roustabout like you."

The fellow was right. Within hours James was carrying loads from a boat to the wharf. Yes, there was plenty of work here.

That evening he wrote his mother. He knew

136

she would be pleased and amused at his news. He had just learned that a priest by the name of Father Galtier had been shocked at the name of this new, thriving town. The priest had decided to rechristen the town "Saint Paul."

James' address now was St. Paul, Territory of Minnesota, the United States of America. "I won't stay in St. Paul very long," he wrote to his mother. Little did he realize that he would stay there for over sixty years.

Young Jim Hill

EVER SINCE James had been thirteen years old, he had called himself James Jerome Hill, but after he reached St. Paul, Minnesota, he became plain Jim Hill. Nobody in this midwest frontier community gave any thought to such matters as middle names. Mainly people were interested only in working hard and looking to the future.

Young Hill's first step after he reached St. Paul was to look about and decide whether or not he wished to stay there. His next step was to secure a position, and he was determined to find a position that he would like. He wanted to use his head as well as his hands.

He contacted several steamboat companies and soon secured a position as agent for a company that handled large quantities of freight on the Mississippi River. He was to become a clerk to look after handling this freight.

Young Hill was supposed to be on hand whenever a company steamboat arrived, night or day, to check the incoming and outgoing freight. The freight had to be loaded and unloaded promptly at the wharf, so that other boats could come to the wharf without causing a congestion.

Many boats reached St. Paul in the night. They arrived at all hours of the night. There was no way of telling when to expect them, but their loud whistles usually let workers and others know that they were coming.

Jim Hill slept on a cot in the office. This saved him from paying rent for an expensive room in town, and it certainly was handy. The moment he heard a whistle sounding down the river, he began to dress. Then by the time the gangplank was pushed out, he was on hand.

Jim Hill checked every barrel, box, or bundle that was carried to or from a boat. He took pride in checking the items promptly, so that the freight could keep moving.

"I know every steamboat by its whistle," he soon said. "I don't even have to look at the name on the pilot house." Then he added with a chuckle, "I also know all the cooks on the river, the good ones and the poor ones."

According to steamboat regulations, clerks were allowed to take meals on board boats that they helped to service. Jim Hill soon knew which cooks made the best flapjacks, fried the best steaks and raw potatoes, and made the best doughnuts. He was always on hand to eat.

Within a few months he wrote his mother that he had a good place to sleep and plenty to eat. "The only time I have to buy a meal," he re-

ported "is when there's no steamboat around. I'm just Scotch enough to wait for one. I've never been close to starvation yet."

Occasionally a steamboat became stuck on a sandbar in the river. Then the captain would shout up to the pilot house, "Avant there, sir! Just wait five minutes until Jim Hill stows his hold." The young man's healthy appetite led to many a jest.

In those days all the steamboats used wood for fuel. One of young Hill's duties was to keep a supply of cordwood for steamboats, so that they could refuel when they came to St. Paul. He stacked the cordwood up in a huge pile on the wharf. Then it would be there ready for the boats when they arrived, day or night. He was proud of his mountain-high pile of wood.

One night there was a downpouring rain in the St. Paul region and no boats came up the river. Young Hill slept through the night, little realizing how heavy the rain really was and how it would affect the river.

At dawn he looked out and was surprised to find that his pile of cordwood on the wharf was gone. He could scarcely believe his eyes. The heavy rain had caused the river to rise and to wash the pile of wood away. Not a single stick of wood could be seen on the water-soaked wharf.

The young man stared aghast at the river. "Pride goeth before a 'fall, for sure," he said as he started to dress.

At this moment a familiar steamboat whistle sounded. The steamboat "Mary Ann" was coming up the river. The captain of the steamer saw the mass of cordwood floating downstream, and realized what had happened.

He decided to have fun with young Hill about the lost wood. "When we pull up," he said, "we'll insist on Jim's having breakfast. Then maybe he'll have strength enough to get us an armful of kindling wood."

Jim was not trapped. Much to the captain's surprise, he had another pile of cordwood on high land which he had saved for an emergency. With a grin of confidence he delivered the wood to the captain's boat.

"I take off my hat to you, Jim," the captain shouted. "You are a bright lad."

"Someday things will be different out here," said Jim. "This part of the country won't depend so much on river boats."

"No?" inquired the captain. "Like what?"

"We'll have railroads," Jim boasted.

"No railroad can ever compete with a river boat," the captain flung back.

Jim did not argue. He went ahead with his work of checking, being careful to make a record of every barrel, box, or parcel which was handled. He knew that the river was important for

144

transportation, but he was becoming interested in railroads to provide transportation. For one thing, the river was frozen during several months of the year. Railroads would be used all the year round.

One day when he was working over his accounts, he heard a strange noise which he could not identify. The noise seemed to continue rather than come and go, like a whistle.

Gradually the noise became louder and more disturbing. Jim wondered whether some beginner was trying to learn to play the bagpipe or whether a cat or some other animal had been hurt and was crying in agony.

He ran to the door, but he could see nothing to account for the sound. Although it was loud, it seemed to be coming from some distance away. "What on earth is that noise?" he asked an old man who was passing.

"Oh, that's Norm Kittson's Red River train

of oxcarts," the man replied. "Kittson is coming back from Fort Garry up north with a load of furs and other goods which he is bringing here to trade and to sell. Also he's bringing mail, since he has a government contract to carry the mail. I reckon he's about two miles away from St. Paul now. You can always hear his oxcarts for at least five miles."

James realized that Mr. Kittson was the man he had hoped to accompany when he came to St. Paul. He returned to his accounts, but he could not concentrate as thoroughly as he had before. He found himself listening to the creaking noise instead of attending to his work.

Finally he couldn't contain his curiosity any longer. He left the office and climbed the highest hill in the city. There he watched from the capitol building which had been built on this hill a few years before.

Far away there appeared a caravan of heavy

carts, pulled by oxen, moving along a rutted road. The carts, which had enormous wheels, were piled high with goods. The turning cartwheels produced a creaking noise, which became louder and louder. Ahead of the carts walked a man, who evidently was the leader of the long train.

Jim ran down the hill and joined the crowd. The long trip from the north must have been exhausting, but bearded Mr. Kittson, dressed in a coonskin cap and doeskin clothing, strode along in front with all the vigor of a boy.

As the train drew near, the bearded leader seemed to let off spurts of enthusiasm. He waved and called greetings to different persons in the crowd. On the other hand, the drivers, who plodded along beside the oxcarts, seemed to be almost completely exhausted.

As the oxtrain gradually came to a halt, Jim pushed his way forward to examine the carts and their contents more closely. His curiosity was aroused by the strength of the carts and he bent down to see how they were built and mounted on their huge wheels. Suddenly he heard a voice beside him say, "What do you think of them? I have a patent on them."

Jim was surprised to find Mr. Kittson standing beside him. He expressed admiration for the carts and for the quality of the pelts with which they were loaded. The two liked each other at once and struck up a conversation.

"I could use a strong young fellow like you," said Mr. Kittson as they parted.

"I'd like to go with you," Jim said promptly. He was interested, not only in the adventure and the pay, but he wanted to see the Red River Valley and to explore the possibilities of different kinds of transportation. He felt that there should be better and faster means of transporting freight than by oxcarts.

148

Minnesota was organized as a territory in 1849, and it became a state in 1858. At the time it became a state, there wasn't a mile of railroad within its boundaries. Congress authorized the new state, however, to give alternate sections of public land to any company that would build a railroad across them.

Jim Hill was excited about railroads and talked about them to anyone who would listen. He strove to interest newcomers in the project, particularly people who came from the East "with a little money to invest."

After a great deal of talking and planning, the Minnesota and Pacific Railroad Company was organized. Its line was to extend from the steamboat wharf in St. Paul to the Falls of St. Anthony, about ten miles away.

The new railroad would have one engine, two boxcars, and a dozen flatcars. It would take months to level the ground and lay the track.

Jim was excited and happy. He often declared that he had arrived in St. Paul during one of the biggest booms in history. In July, 1856, there were about forty thousand people in the city. By the end of the year the incoming pioneers had swelled the population of the city to one hundred thousand.

July marked the height of the season, with Mississippi River Steamboats bringing in settlers on every trip. The hotels and rooming houses were so crowded that people set up tents on the streets, and nobody minded.

"We've got to make hay while the sun shines," Jim said over and over to his friends. He realized that five long months of winter lay ahead, with the river frozen and navigation closed. He felt that it was unfortunate for all transportation to come to a halt during these months. More and more he became convinced that railroads were the only answer to this problem.

He noted with satisfaction that many settlers were coming from the New England States or from New York State, and he felt certain that more would follow. He predicted that many immigrants, now in the East, including Swedes, Norwegians, and Finns, soon would move farther West. How could anyone resist the "richest soil in the world," offered by the United States Government at one dollar an acre?

Often when a newcomer came to town, he said, "You are lucky to come to this part of the world. We have many opportunities here which you will discover and appreciate later."

Jim made frequent trips to Fort Snelling, White Bear Lake, and other places to the northwest in Minnesota. He became so enthusiastic about the opportunities in these areas that he dropped the idea of going to the Red River settlement. He decided to stay in St. Paul and become a part of this larger community.

Some day, of course, he would hop a freighter for the Orient, but for the time being, he was content to remain in St. Paul. He managed to make a good living, meet many interesting people, and make some plans for the future. He failed to realize that times could change, and that the country could be faced with a financial panic. All the while he felt that prosperity would be continuous and that each new year would be better than the year before. Soon he would learn differently by a hard turn of events.

A financial panic started in 1857, when a large New York bank closed its doors. In a short time other banks in other cities closed their doors. People and business firms that had done business with these banks were not allowed to withdraw their money.

Minnesota was very hard hit. Many people had borrowed money to invest in different kinds of business and had hoped that their investments would make them rich. They were in debt, but so long as business was booming, they could earn money to pay back what they owed.

Now, suddenly money was cut off and banks demanded that people repay the money which they owed. Settlers who had flocked to St. Paul a few months before now moved away. Soon the population was only half as large as it had been at the height of prosperity.

All the country in the Mid-West was affected by the panic. The farmers had borowed money at banks to buy farm machinery. They had hoped to use this machinery to cultivate more acres of land than they had cultivated before. Now they were faced with the prospect of losing the machinery and not cultivating the land.

Explorations
and Romance

"So you think railroads can compete with steamboats," people frequently said to Jim Hill, as the owners of the small Minnesota and Pacific Railroad struggled to make the railroad profitable. Men frequently gathered in the railroad office near the wharves.

"Maybe I'm stubborn," Jim would retort to his challengers, "but I still think that railroads have a great future."

By now the ten miles of track had been laid from the steamboat landing in St. Paul to the Falls of St. Anthony on the Mississippi River. A small engine pulled cars back and forth on

154

tracks but the cars carried few passengers and little freight. The situation seemed discouraging to everybody except Jim.

"I don't know what we're going to do about passenger traffic," the conductor complained one day at the end of a run. "We get occasional passengers, but when I ask for their fares, they jump off at the next siding. Do you suppose the time will ever come when people will want to ride trains? And will people ever be willing to pay fares for riding?"

"Yes, the time will come when people will ride trains in great numbers," replied Jim hopefully. "They'll travel from station to station, from state to state, and even from the Atlantic Ocean to the Pacific Ocean and back."

"I'm also worried about freight," said the conductor. "The farmers are content to haul their grain to mill in wagons in the summer and on sleds in the winter. Lumbermen cut trees in the forests during the winter and float them down river in the spring."

"Times will change," retorted Jim.

By now investors were interested in the government regulation which permitted railroad companies to sell land to help pay the cost of building railroads. Many surveyors came to Minnesota to plot sections of land.

When winter came and the river froze over, St. Paul became very quiet. There was no business to speak of and no heartening sound of steamboat whistles. "Everybody stays inside during the winter," Jim wrote home. "Tell Professor Wetherald I am reading Roman history on a steamer frozen in the river."

Jim always found plenty to do during the day. He realized that everybody needed wood for fuel during the long winter to heat their homes and business places.

Accordingly he and a grizzled partner, Sam

Griggs, went into the business of buying and selling cordwood. They hired the cordwood cut from trees in the forest and then resold it to persons in the city. Some of the cordwood they sold to the railroad company for fuel.

Jim even managed to get the railroad and steamboats to work together. Young as he was, he got steamboats to bring coal up the river for the railroad. The coal was mined near Peoria in central Illinois, loaded on barges, and floated down the Illinois River to the Mississippi River. Then it was loaded on steamboats and brought up the river to St. Paul.

Many people laughed at the idea of bringing coal to a part of the country where there was an abundance of wood. Gradually, however, people began to use the coal in place of wood.

Soon after their first meeting, Norman Kittson and Jim Hill became good friends. Jim, now in his early twenties, sometimes went through the Red River Valley with the Kittson team. Occasionally during the winter, when there was a rush of freight, he made trips with dog teams for his friend. On his trips over the wilds of northern United States and southern Canada, he gained first-hand knowledge of the territory. He found this information very helpful later, after he began to build railroads.

On one of his trips with dog teams, Jim had a dangerous adventure. He was accompanied by a half-breed of bad character as a guide. While they were traveling in the open country, the half-breed suggested that they head for Lake Superior and divide their cargo.

Jim refused and the guide grew ugly. Each of them had a rifle and knife, but Jim did not want to risk a fight with the fellow. As they traveled on, however, the guide became uglier and changed his suggestions to commands.

Before long they came to a high ridge, where they could see many miles over the dazzling snow. Jim pretended that he needed to adjust the harness on his dogs, and managed to get about forty feet away from the half-breed. Then he cocked his rifle, got a bead on the fellow's

159

back, and ordered him to hold up his hands. The guide had no choice but to obey. Jim had to use a rifle left-handed because of his blind right eye, but he was a sure shot and a quick one. His companion knew it and willingly obeyed.

Jim ordered the half-breed to start walking out over the ridge all by himself. Then he picked up the fellow's rifle and knife and went on alone with the dog team.

By now Jim could afford to patronize the Merchant's Hotel, the luxury hotel of St. Paul. Back in town after his hazardous trip with the dog team, he met old Sam Griggs, his partner in the wood business. He and Sam had breakfast together one morning at the hotel.

Jim told Sam about his adventure with the half-breed. Sam loved a good story and proved to be an appreciative audience. "I can just see that Indian high-tailing it toward the river," he chuckled in return.

While Jim was telling his story to Sam, the waitress at the hotel had listened intently. She was a very intelligent girl with beautiful dark eyes, shining black hair, rosy cheeks, and a slim graceful figure. Jim knew that she had heard him telling the story.

Soon she spoke to Jim, using very precise language which attracted Jim's attention. "Mr. Hill, didn't it worry you to turn that poor man adrift on the frozen plain without a gun to defend himself?" she asked. "What if wolves had followed him over the barren land?"

"No, it didn't worry me," Jim replied bluntly. "He had shown his colors, and he had this punishment coming. Besides, he probably struck an Indian village within fifty miles."

As the waitress turned away without answering, Jim said, "That girl has a streak of tenderness in her. She's even concerned over a scoundrel who probably would have killed me."

"Maybe she could even learn to like you," Sam Griggs said with a grin.

In 1867, young Hill, still in his twenties, obtained a position with a larger steamboat company on the Mississippi River and became an agent for the St. Paul and Pacific Railroad. "With the railroad running past my door," he reasoned wisely, "I will find it easy to serve both the steamboat company and the railroad."

Now he had two jobs. He had to tend to the incoming and outgoing freight of steamboats. Even more important, he had to get business for the railroad. Luckily he had friends who would help him secure business.

He and some of his friends often ate lunch together at a favorite table in the hotel dining room. While they were eating, they discussed different ways of building up the country. One idea, like building a railroad to the Pacific, was fabulous but not impossible.

The friends often played little jokes on one another. One noon Jim stood up as the group lingered over coffee. "Gentlemen," he said, "do you remember Mary, the charming young lady who used to wait on our table? She was as Irish and as lovely as the Emerald Isle." All the men nodded. Of course they remembered her.

"I hear she is about to be married," Jim continued. "It would be only fitting and proper to pass the hat to give her a little Christmas present. I'll start off."

Jim's contribution was so generous that the others could hardly hold back. Then after he had completed the collection, someone innocently asked, "Who is the lucky fellow that is going to get Mary for a wife?"

"Me!" Jim shouted in glee. "Me, of course. I thank you for our dowry."

"Now Mary can really start off in elegance," one of the friends commented.

Mary was not the kind to spend money foolishly. She wanted to obtain more education and used this money to attend a new school which was being opened in St. Paul by the Sisters of Notre Dame. The sisters at the school taught her to translate French, to write proper letters, and to create lovely needlework in wool and beads.

Jim and Mary were content to live very simply after they were married. They started to keep house in a small cottage in the city. Little did they dream that some day they would live in a mansion on a fashionable street.

Successful
Young
Businessman

By now Hill had built a reputation for being a hard-working, dependable young man with good business acumen. People respected him and gradually began to call him Mr. James Jerome Hill rather than plain Jim Hill.

Young Mr. Hill became an expert at fixing freight rates and brought much new business to the railroad company. He knew much about the country in the Northwest and the opportunities to open up larger areas for settlement. Presently vast areas were virtually uninhabited, except by scattered tribes of Indians.

Most businessmen believed that many years

would pass before this vast open country would be settled. Young Mr. Hill, however, felt that the area could be settled fairly soon. He began to foresee a vast fertile area filled with people who would have railroads extending here and there to supply their needs.

He had watched the building of the ten miles of railroad track between St. Paul and St. Anthony with great interest. Now that he was working for the railroad he understood some of its problems and difficulties. So far this was the only railroad operating within the whole state of Minnesota.

The owners had borrowed more than two million dollars to build the railroad, and Mr. Hill thought that at least half of the amount had been wasted. The track was poorly laid, and many rails lay rusting along the roadbed. When the train finally began to operate, the little steam engine had to depend on wood for fuel, which made it difficult to keep up steam. The train moved slowly along the tracks with no attempt to maintain a schedule. There were frequent accidents caused by a failing engine or broken rails.

The owners had spent all the money they could get to build the railroad. When the train began to operate, they had hoped to make enough profit to begin paying off their debt. Instead, they had incurred huge losses month after month. Now it became apparent that the railroad would have to have more miles of track and serve more people to be profitable.

Mr. Hill and Mr. Griggs, his partner in the wood business, supplied cordwood for the engine, and maintained huge piles at the ends of the line. All the while Mr. Hill believed that coal would make better fuel for the engine.

Mr. Hill gave considerable thought to the problem of securing coal, and he made a thorough survey of coal deposits within several hundred miles. He even leased large tracts of land in areas where coal was known to exist.

During this time Mr. Hill was rapidly increasing his business interests. He now owned a warehouse, a steamboat and flatboats, and was trading successfully over a large area. He was gaining experience in business dealings, meeting outstanding businessmen with whom he would have important dealings later, and laying the foundation for a prosperous future.

In the meantime the owners of the St. Paul and Pacific Railroad had been able to borrow money and extend the tracks almost three hundred miles westward. All the while they continued to operate the railroad badly as before. Many knew that the line was headed for disaster.

Meanwhile other railroad companies were building tracks and extending lines in the north-central parts of our country. Most of these railroads, like the St. Paul and Pacific Railroad, were poorly constructed and managed and extended only a few hundred miles through the country. Mr. Hill still dreamed of great railroad systems that would connect all parts of the country. He believed that railroads in the northern part of our country would take the place of slow, inefficient oxcarts, dog sleds, and river boats. He realized that they would have a great advantage because trains could run all months of the year. Up to now, however, he had had no opportunity to put his dreams to use.

In 1873, another panic, far more serious than the one in 1857, hit the country. This panic, which stranded business, was by far the worst financial disaster that our country had ever experienced up to that time.

The panic began with the failure of a large bank in Philadelphia. Other banks in different parts of the country closed within a few days. Then steel mills, lumber companies, and other

169

businesses came to a standstill. Rairoad construction was stopped, and many railroad companies, including the St. Paul and Pacific, failed. People were restless and many were penniless.

This financial panic, which bewildered many people, failed to disturb Mr. Hill. He had learned how big business operated, and felt that he knew some of the weaknesses and pitfalls. Through the years he had expanded his own business interests, but he had been careful to build securely. Now he felt safe financially even in the midst of a terrifying national panic.

Mr. Hill had been eager for years to own a railroad. He had often told his friend, Norman Kittson, of his interest, but he had obtained little support. Now he saw an opportunity to get control of the St. Paul and Pacific Railroad, which was bankrupt.

He was fairly rich for a man of his age, but he didn't have nearly enough money by himself.

"This is our chance to get control of the St. Paul and Pacific Railroad and run it the way it should be run," he told Mr. Kittson. "The persons who loaned money to the railroad will be glad to get back a little of the money which they have invested instead of none at all."

"Jim, if we risk every dollar we can raise, our combined fortunes will make only a small part of the money we need to buy the railroad," Kittson exclaimed. "It's impossible."

"We'll find men who have money and will be willing to invest," Hill declared.

"Men with money won't be interested in investing money in this small, badly built, badly managed, bankrupt railroad," Kittson said firmly. "You and I know that we could make the railroad pay. We've both been in the business of carrying goods most of our lives. But we can't raise the money to buy the railroad."

"Yes we can," said Mr. Hill. "Then we'll

build a network of railroads to fill the country with people and look after their needs. We'll bring in goods from the East and send goods to the East. This land will support millions of people, instead of just a few fur trappers. We'll build cities and villages along the way and divide the land into farms for producing wheat and corn for raising cattle."

"All right, Jim," Kittson said wearily. "I'll risk everything I have to buy this little poorly-built, bankrupt railroad, if you'll do the same. But I don't think we can find any rich business-men foolish enough to invest millions of dollars in the venture with us."

At this time the Canadian Pacific Railroad was being built from east to west, across the southern part of Canada. Two men who were largely responsible for building this line were Donald Smith and George Stephen. Mr. Hill and Mr. Kittson had done business with Mr. Smith.

Soon Mr. Smith came to St. Paul on business and Mr. Hill promptly got in touch with him. He presented Mr. Smith with facts and figures on the St. Paul and Pacific Railroad. He persuaded Mr. Smith that the railroad could be bought for half what it was worth, run profitably, and extended to connect with other railroads.

"My cousin, George Stephen, is president of a large bank in Montreal," said Mr. Smith. "He controls more money than any other man in Canada. Why don't you go to Montreal with me and talk to him? If he would join the rest of us, we might be able to swing the deal."

Mr. Hill went with Mr. Smith to Montreal and presented facts and figures showing the present value of the St. Paul and Pacific and the cost of the network of railroads he hoped to build. This would include a line to connect with the Canadian Pacific. The railroads would bring thousands of people to the Northwest, including

Canada, who would settle the land and help to build the railroads. In later years the railroads would bring them what they needed to buy and would carry their produce away to market.

This is just what Mr. Stephen and Mr. Smith wanted to do. They could readily foresee a time when there would be well-developed farms, and cities, with stores, factories, and flour mills, where now there were endless forests and prairies. They could foresee an opportunity to develop copper mines, iron and coal mines, and to make use of the forests.

Mr. Stephen came with several experts to look over the St. Paul and Pacific Railroad. After he had investigated it thoroughly, he agreed to try to raise the money to purchase the railroad. This would probably require some little time, possibly as much as two or three years.

The railroad was finally reorganized as the St. Paul, Minneapolis, and Manitoba Railroad.

Mr. Stephen was made president and Mr. Kittson and Mr. Smith were made vice presidents. Mr. Hill was made general manager.

Mr. Hill soon found that he had a very difficult job. Many unforeseen bills against the bankrupt railroad began to pour in. Apparently the former owners had not paid for locomotives, railroad tracks or ties, timber, or anything else they had purchased. At the same time the newly reorganized railroad needed to purchase large amounts of materials for expansion.

The government offered large grants of land to companies that would build and operate railroads by a certain date. The companies, in turn, were to sell the land to settlers at low prices. The money from the land would help to pay for building the railroads.

The old St. Paul and Pacific Railroad had been granted land, but still had failed to build tracks across 68 miles of the land. Now the time was about up, and Mr. Hill, as manager of the new company had to build these 68 miles of track or lose the land. He also had to keep the locomotives running on the old railroad and at the same time, practically rebuild tracks.

He also had to build 160 miles of track to connect the St. Paul, Minneapolis, and Manitoba Railroad with the Canadian Pacific Railroad. There was no time limit on this, but he knew a rival railroad would build the track if he did not get it done immediately.

During this difficult period, Mr. Hill's chief goal was to save the land grant. For a time the company would have to depend on the money which it received from the sale of land to build tracks and operate the railroad.

James J. Hill, Empire Builder

UNDER James J. Hill's efficient management, the St. Paul, Minneapolis and Manitoba Railroad completed its tracks within the allotted time. He persuaded the government to approve of its bankrupt condition so that he could use the new funds for expansion.

At the same time he dealt successfully with a rival railroad, that used tracks belonging to the St. Paul, Minneapolis, and Manitoba Railroad. He felt that the other company should pay higher rates for using the tracks or build tracks of its own. Accordingly, he increased the rates for the privilege of using the tracks and for

178

storing freight belonging to the other company at stations along the line.

The directors of the rival company looked at one another in amazement. They hadn't expected this action from the manager of the bankrupt railroad. Now they found that they would have to pay a fair share of the upkeep.

Mr. Hill gradually went ahead with his plans to extend the railroad through open country farther west. Already the government had promised much of the land along the route to another railroad company. This company, however, had not proceeded to lay tracks along the route to open up the country.

This failure on the part of the other railroad led Mr. Hill to feel that his company should step in and take its place. He felt that since the company had failed to proceed, the government should grant the land to him.

Finally he made an agreement with the other

company, under which it could use the tracks of the St. Paul, Minneapolis, and Manitoba Railroad to haul freight over the line. In return the other company agreed not to extend its tracks just to provide competition.

At last Mr. Hill had an opportunity to make plans for a company and to bear responsibilities that he liked. He found managing the railroad a challenging adventure, even though he was constantly faced with unforeseen problems.

During this period he went out along the right-of-way and directed the extension of the railroad rather than sit in his office and issue orders. He made all the plans with the help of his assistants and actually directed the details of construction.

By now many other railroad lines were being built in the United States. Many were being built poorly and would have to be rebuilt or abandoned. Mr. Hill was determined to build his tracks right from the beginning. He had the land thoroughly explored so that he could lay tracks through the best passes in the mountains. He had specialists check the locations of rich farm land, forests, and possible mines, which would help to bring business to the railroad after it had been built.

He sent surveyors ahead to map the route of the railroad. He kept crews ready to grade the land and to build the bridges. Then the rails could be laid and spiked down quickly.

One constant problem was to secure adequate workers, and another was to secure adequate materials. Mr. Hill had to have hundreds of workers at the end of the line to keep pushing ahead, and he had to make certain that he had plenty of rails, ties, and other materials for laying the tracks.

Under his efficient direction the workers usually could lay a mile of track a day, and sometimes more. Workers constantly had to be replaced, because many suffered accidents or illnesses, or became dissatisfied with the long hours, heartbreaking work, or unfortunate living conditions. The work was difficult and boring, with little change from day to day.

The workers suffered many physical hardships in the isolated construction camps. Early in the summer they were tortured by swarms of biting mosquitoes. A little later they suffered from high temperatures during the working hours. Many fainted as they attempted to work.

Often the workers became ill from drinking contaminated water from streams, the only water available. Other were bitten by rattlesnakes, which were very numerous.

The suffering was even greater during the winter. The workers continually suffered from frostbitten ears, faces, hands, and feet. They slept in tents, which gave little protection from

182

wind, hail, sleet, and snow. Often the men huddled about fires in boxcars.

Despite these hard working conditions, many men continued to work for Mr. Hill year after year. They liked him, believed in him, and felt that he was treating them fairly. Among other things, they liked him because he remembered their names. Sometimes when they were ill, he would even take over their construction work.

Always he wanted the workers to feel that even though he was the manager, he still was a friend. They liked him because he worked along with them and suffered the same hardships.

Year after year the extension continued westward, first to meet the Canadian Pacific tracks, then on through the Dakotas and Montana, and finally in 1893 to Oregon and the Pacific Coast. The new railroad included two thousand miles of track, making it one of the longest railroads in the country. In its great sweep across the northern part of our country, it helped to convert a vast area of wilderness into lands later to become worth billions of dollars.

Almost immediately immigrants from the eastern part of our country and from Europe began to settle along the new railroad. They came in large numbers, just as Mr. Hill had predicted they would, when he first became interested in railroads as a means of transportation. Under his management the railroad offered settlers many inducements to come to this part of the country. It sold land reasonably to the settlers and provided them with cheap transportation.

Most of the newcomers who settled along the new railroad built homes and began to till the soil. Some of them knew very little about growing crops on farms. They planted wheat on much of the land, which seemed to be the best crop to grow in that part of the country. Every now and then there was too little spring rain to help the wheat get started or too little later to help it grow and mature.

Mr. Hill from his own boyhood experiences in Canada knew a great deal about farming, and he had always been interested in farming. He considered the farmers who settled along his railroad as friends, and he was eager to help them in every way possible. Moreover, he knew that the railroad could not succeed without them. The more the farmers raised, the more products they would send to markets on the railroad. The railroad needed them.

As Mr. Hill studied the farm situation, he concluded that the farmers were depending too much on growing wheat. He felt that they would be more prosperous, if they grew more kinds of crops and raised more farm animals, including cattle, hogs, and sheep. Most of the farmers kept few animals and these were very

185

poor. The cows gave little milk and the steers and hogs were scrawny.

To encourage the farmers, Mr. Hill sent to England for better breeds of cattle and he brought in better breeds of workhorses for the farms. He helped the farmers to secure better seed for planting crops and better machinery for cultivating and harvesting the crops. He helped them to get longtime loans at reasonable rates of interest.

He felt that even poor quality land could be profitable. Accordingly, he set up a model farm in northern Minnesota to try out some of his ideas about improved farming.

In addition, he provided reports to show how farmers could make the best possible uses of their land, what crops and animals they could raise most profitably. He sent many boys to agricultural schools for short courses to help them learn about farming.

186

Gradually the farmers began to grow additional crops and to raise a variety of animals on their farms. When the wheat crop was small, they still had corn, cattle, hogs, sheep, and dairy products to sell. They shipped all these products to markets on the railroad, just as Mr. Hill had predicted some years before.

Even though the farmers raised many things to sell, wheat continued to be the most important crop. In early days flour mills had been built in the little town of St. Anthony, which later became Minneapolis. These mills ground wheat and other grain for the farmers round about. As railroads were built, other flour mills were built from Minneapolis westward.

The long railroad, which Mr. Hill completed in 1893, was the first transcontinental railroad built without government aid. The railroad received government land grants only for building the first few hundred miles of track. The cost of building the railroad across the Dakotas, Montana, the Rocky Mountains, and on to the Pacific Coast had to be obtained by other means.

As an official of the railroad, Mr. Hill advanced rapidly. First he moved up from manager to vice-president. Then from 1892 until 1907 he served as president, after which he was chairman of the board for several years.

By the end of 1884, Mr. Hill had increased the railroad tracks hundreds of miles. In 1891 he helped to found the Great Northern Railroad to include all the railroad lines that he and his associates had built or acquired.

At this time Mr. Hill could readily borrow money for expansion, because he never had tried to borrow more than he needed and he had always paid his obligations on time. Thus the new railroad started off in good financial condition from the beginning.

The Great Northern Railroad became one of

the largest railroad companies in America, noted for its fine business operations. There was a severe business panic in 1893 which caused many railroads to go bankrupt. The Great Northern, however, kept on thriving and paid dividends to its stockholders as usual, and it kept on paying dividends regularly.

During his long life Mr. Hill acquired a large fortune. He built a beautiful mansion in St. Paul, which included a library, an art gallery, and even a theater. The library contained original volumes by some of the world's leading authors, and the art gallery original paintings by some of the world's leading painters.

Through the years Hill was ever helpful to the other members of his family and to his boyhood friends in Rockwell, Canada. One of the most touching events in his life was the privilege of entertaining his beloved boyhood teacher, Professor Wetherald, in St. Paul.

Hill gave generously of his money for many worthy causes. He built a famous reference library for the residents of St. Paul. He helped to establish a seminary in St. Paul for the training of priests in the Catholic Church.

Regardless of his success he never became haughty. He always enjoyed mingling with people, whatever their stations in life. Often, as president of the Great Northern Railroad, he traveled in a private car. One time the train became stalled in a blizzard in the Northwest. The crew on the train tried to shovel the snow from the tracks so the train could proceed.

He was not content to stand by and watch the members work by themselves. He grabbed a shovel from one of the men and said, "Go into the car and get some hot coffee." One after another he relieved the members of the crew in this way.

Hill and his beloved wife Mary raised a distinguished family of three sons and seven daughters. The sons followed closely in their father's footsteps. Louis became president of the Great Northern Railroad. James became vice-president of the Northern Pacific Railroad. Walter took charge of iron mining properties near Lake Superior and in the Red River Valley.

The seven daughters of the family were Mary, Clara, Catherine, Charlotte, Ruth, Rachel, and Gertrude. All were noted for their beauty, their civic interests, and their charities. They possessed the great Hill hospitality and gave freely to the needy.

In later years James Jerome Hill came to be known as the "Empire Builder," because of leadership in building up a new part of our country. No person in history has ever made a greater contribution of this nature.

More About This Book

WHEN JAMES J. HILL LIVED

1838   JAMES J. HILL WAS BORN NEAR ROCKWOOD, ONTARIO, CANADA, SEPTEMBER 16.

There were twenty-six states in the Union.

Martin Van Buren was President.

The population of the country was about 16,230,000.

1838–   JAMES GREW UP, ATTENDED SCHOOL, AND
1856   WORKED TO HELP SUPPORT HIS FAMILY.

The first trans-Atlantic steamship service was inaugurated, 1840.

The Mexican War was fought, 1846-1848.

Gold was discovered in California, 1848.

1856–   YOUNG HILL CAME TO THIS COUNTRY AND FI-
1867   NALLY SETTLED IN ST. PAUL, MINNESOTA.

The Lincoln-Douglas debates were held, 1858.

The War between the States was fought, 1861-1865.

President Abraham Lincoln was assassinated and Andrew Johnson became President, 1865.

193

1867–
1878   HILL BECAME INTERESTED IN RAILROADS AS AN
       IMPORTANT MEANS OF TRANSPORTATION.

The United States purchased Alaska, 1867.

The first transcontinental railroad was completed, 1869.

Alexander Bell invented the telephone, 1876.

Bicycles were first made in America, 1878.

1878–
1893   HILL AND ASSOCIATES PURCHASED AND EX-
       TENDED THE ST. PAUL AND PACIFIC RAILROAD.

Thomas Edison invented the phonograph, 1878, and the electric light bulb, 1879.

The first electric railway in this country was operated in Baltimore, 1885.

Henry Ford built his first gas engine, 1893.

1893–
1916   HILL DEVELOPED THE NORTHWEST AND BE-
       CAME KNOWN AS THE "EMPIRE BUILDER."

The Spanish-American War was fought, 1898.

Wilbur and Orville Wright flew the first heavier-than-air aircraft, 1903.

Robert Peary discovered the North Pole, 1909.

The Panama Canal was completed and opened to world traffic, 1914.

1916 JAMES J. HILL DIED IN ST. PAUL, MINNESOTA, MAY 29.

There were forty-eight states in the Union.

Woodrow Wilson was President.

The population of the country was about 100,220,000.

DO YOU REMEMBER?

1. What did the Hill family do when the big oak tree fell near the log-cabin home?

2. How did Lady and her new colt Star help to bring joy to the Hill family?

3. How did James happen to lose the complete sight of his right eye?

4. What road building did James undertake in order to purchase the colt Star?

5. How did James demonstrate great ability during the spelldown contest at school?

6. What work did different members of the Hill family do at the Rockwood Inn?

7. How did members of the family become acquainted with many people at the inn?

8. What great tragedy came to the Hill family on Christmas Day, 1852?

9. How did James take over as head of the Hill family following his father's death?

10. Why did James decide to come to the United States to seek his fortune?

11. Why did James become just plain Jim Hill after he started to work in St. Paul?

12. How did young Hill find out more about the country outside St. Paul in Minnesota?

13. How did Hill become manager of the St. Paul, Minneapolis, and Manitoba Railroad?

14. How did Hill continue to achieve success in the later years of his life?

IT'S FUN TO LOOK UP THESE THINGS

1. Why was St. Paul well situated to become an important early trading center?

2. When and where was the first railroad built in this country?

3. When was the first continental railroad in this country completed?

196

4. Why was the telegraph once very important to railroads?

5. How did George Westinghouse help to improve railroad transportation?

6. How does a modern diesel locomotive differ from a steam locomotive?

INTERESTING THINGS YOU CAN DO

1. Trace on a map the route of the Great Northern Railroad.

2. Gather photographs of old locomotives and railroad cars for an exhibit.

3. Make a drawing or a model of a modern diesel locomotive.

4. Name the railroads that pass through your city or your part of the country.

5. Make a list of the most important railroads in this country today.

6. Prepare a report telling why railroads provide an important type of transportation.

7. Describe a ride or a trip which you have taken on a passenger train.

OTHER BOOKS YOU MAY ENJOY READING

Andrew Carnegie: Young Steelmaker, Joanne Landers Henry. Trade and School Editions, Bobbs-Merrill.

Building of the First Transcontinental Railroad, Adele Nathan. Random House.

Diesel-Electric 4030, Henry Billings. Viking.

Railroads in the Days of Steam, Albert L. McCready and Lawrence W. Sagle. Harper.

Railroads: Today and Yesterday, Walter Buehr. Putnam.

Trains, Robert Selph Henry. Bobbs-Merrill.

INTERESTING WORDS IN THIS BOOK

acumen (ă kū′měn) : keenness in intellectual or business matters

alternate (ôl′tĕr nĭt) : every other one

audible (ô′dĭ b'l) : within sound

bankrupt (băngk′rŭpt) : unable to pay debts

contaminated (kŏn tăm′ĭ nāt ĕd) : unfit for use, spoiled, polluted

corduroy road (kôr′dŭ roi) : road made of logs laid crosswise

distraught (dĭs trôt') : agitated by grief or worry, distressed, crazed

dividends (dĭv'ĭ dĕnz) : money distributed to stockholders from profits of a business

embarrassment (ĕm băr'ăs mĕnt) : chagrin, feeling of self-consciousness

enthusiastic (ĕn thū'zĭ ăs'tik) : filled with strong favorable feeling

epidemic (ĕp'ĭ dĕm'ĭc) : outbreak of a disease with many people sick at the same time

gangplank (găng'plăngk') : movable bridge-like platform used for boarding or leaving a ship

greedy (grēd'ĭ) : wanting more than one's share

hazardous (hăz'ēr dŭs) : dangerous, risky

heritage (hĕr'ĭ tĭj) : legacy, anything received from an ancestor

immigrant (ĭm'ĭ grănt) : person who comes into a country from another country to live

investigate (ĭn vĕs'tĭ gāt) : look into or examine closely

laggard (lăg'ērd) : person who falls behind

migrate (mī'grāt) : move from one country or place to another

mortgage (môr'gĭj) : indebtedness on property, such as land and buildings

199

obligation (ŏb'lĭ gā'shŭn) : debt, responsibility for value received

optic (ŏp'tĭk) : pertaining to the eye

philosophy (fĭ lŏs'ŏ fĭ) : principles for proper everyday living, wisdom

reorganize (rē ôr'găn īz) : change the structure of a business

roustabout (roust'ȧ bout') : wharf laborer or deck hand, especially on a river steamboat

rutabaga (rōō'tȧ bā'gȧ) : root vegetable

scoundrel (skoun'drĕl) : mean, worthless person, person with a bad reputation

stockholder: person who has invested money in a business enterprise

surgeon (sûr'jŭn) : doctor who specializes in performing operations

survey (sẽr vā') : determine the location and boundaries of a tract of land

uninhabited (ŭn'ĭn hăb'ĭt ĕd) : unoccupied, not lived in or on

vegetate (vĕj'ė tāt) : do little but eat and grow, stay in one place

vigorous (vĭg'ẽr ŭs) : strong, robust, energetic

wharf (hwôrf) : platform built on the shore or out from shore for loading and unloading ships